2

THE AUDIENCE OF
BEOWULF

THE AUDIENCE OF
BEOWULF

BY

DOROTHY WHITELOCK

FELLOW OF ST. HILDA'S COLLEGE, OXFORD

OXFORD
AT THE CLARENDON PRESS
1951

Oxford University Press, Amen House, London E.C.4

GLASGOW NEW YORK TORONTO MELBOURNE WELLINGTON
BOMBAY CALCUTTA MADRAS CAPE TOWN

Geoffrey Cumberlege, Publisher to the University

PRINTED IN GREAT BRITAIN

PREFACE

THE three lectures that follow were delivered at the invitation of the University of London in the Senate House in January and February 1950. They make no claim to be an exhaustive study of *Beowulf*, but merely consider some of its problems from a particular approach. This has necessitated the repeating of much that has often been said before, and no attempt is made to refer to previous writers on matters which are now universally accepted, for this could hardly have been done without writing much of the history of *Beowulf* scholarship in footnote form. In order to keep the footnotes within reasonable bounds I have confined them to references to original authorities, or to studies on the topics with which I have been specifically concerned.

I should like to express my gratitude to Sir Frank Stenton, Dr. K. Sisam, and Professor B. Dickins for reading this work in manuscript and giving me much helpful criticism and advice; to Miss B. Hill, of St. Hilda's College, for valuable help with the proofs; and to the staff of the Clarendon Press for the care and speed with which they have produced this book.

D. W.

ST. HILDA'S COLLEGE
OXFORD
9 September 1950

NOTE

Unless it is otherwise stated, references in the footnotes by line refer to *Beowulf*; Chambers, means R. W. Chambers, *Beowulf: An Introduction*, 2nd edition, Cambridge, 1932; Klaeber, F. Klaeber, *Beowulf and the Fight at Finnsburg*, 3rd edition, revised, Boston, 1941.

I

FROM time to time in *Beowulf* studies it is desirable to do a sort of stock-taking, to see if received opinions have stood the test of time and the impact of new evidence. It is a salutary undertaking even if, at the end, we should find ourselves very much where we were before; for we can then go on to build on the old foundations with increased confidence. It may be that more positive results will be forthcoming from the investigation, that new matter can be added to that kernel of material which it is safe to regard as the established fact of *Beowulf* scholarship; or, on the other hand, that some material can be shown to be masquerading as established fact when it should still be regarded as open to doubt. It sometimes happens that a well-argued theory, with the authority of a great scholar behind it, will, after a series of progressive repetitions by others who ignore the safeguards and reservations of the original propounder, acquire an axiomatic quality which that propounder would have been the first to deplore; and then, being handed on as incontrovertible fact, which it is not, it may block the line of advance and stand in the way of the true assessment of new evidence as this comes to light. It is in no mood of disparagement of the work of any scholars of the past, that I propose to re-examine a few of the basic problems of *Beowulf* scholarship, in relation to any available new factors. Such factors may be the product of work in other fields of learning, and there is sometimes a time-lag before it is realized that their reverberations reach our poem.

And why my title? It will seem very trite and obvious to say that the effect of any work of art depends not only on the author's power and skill, but also on what is already present in the minds of its hearers, or readers, or—in the case of the visual arts—its beholders. Nevertheless, this consideration is particularly pertinent to the poem of *Beowulf,* partly because it is far removed from us in time, so that we are not entitled to assume without investigation that an audience of the poet's day would be moved by the same things as we are, or, if by the same things, in the same way; but still more, because much of the poem is composed with a subtle technique of allusion, reminder, and suggestion, so that we cannot guess at the effect the poet was hoping to obtain unless we know something of the meaning and associations his hints and allusions carried to those for whom he composed his poem. This is, of course, no new idea: it is implicit in most *Beowulf* scholarship, though occasionally writers have lost sight of it. Yet it seems to me that the contribution of the audience to the full understanding of the poem is so important that it is time that for once it should be allowed to get on to a title-page. I propose, in these three chapters, to focus attention on to it.

There may be persons who are content to study the impression that the poem makes now, concerning themselves only with what has survived the changes in our civilization and methods of thought, and caring little that ignorance of what the author counted on his audience knowing robs many of his remarks of their point. The poet has perhaps conveyed something of permanent value that is above the accidents of time and place and has survived the ravages of the centuries. I think he has. It is not for me to discuss the legitimacy of such an approach, but it is not such persons that I am addressing. For my own part, I should like to know what effect the poet was consciously striving to produce on the men of his own time; I want to see if by studying these men we can get any nearer to that knowledge. It will be necessary in the first place to gather what we can about them from the poem's statements and implications; but this does not mean that I wish to use the poem merely as a quarry for social history. I propose to use the poem of *Beowulf* to elucidate the poem of *Beowulf*.

First, however, I must define what I mean by the 'poet' and the 'audience' of *Beowulf*. By the 'poet' I designate the Christian author who was responsible for giving the poem the general shape and tone in which it has survived, and by the 'audience' the people whom he had in mind. It is as well to admit that one cannot prove beyond question that there never was a heathen poem on *Beowulf*. It is difficult to prove a negative, and we cannot know in what form the older materials which the Christian author undoubtedly used were available to him. But one can show that, if a heathen poem on this subject once existed, it must have been very different from the work that has come down to us. As has often been pointed out, the Christian element is not merely superimposed; it permeates the poem. It is not confined to a few—or even to a number—of pious ejaculations in the author's own person or in the mouths of his characters; an acceptance of the Christian order of things is implicit throughout the poem. It pervades the very imagery: the sun is 'heaven's candle' or 'the bright beacon of God', the spring thaw comes when 'the Father unbinds the fetters of the pool'. If there once was an original *Beowulf* from which all this was lacking, a poet—no mere scribe—has gone to the trouble of completely re-thinking and revising the work, and it is with the audience for whose benefit he did this that I am concerned, not with the hypothetical audience of a postulated earlier work. I do not, however, wish to maintain that the poem has been immune from modification during the period that separates this Christian author from the date of the extant manuscript. It is hardly likely that it should have become so stereotyped that any change was impossible; nevertheless the work makes on me, as it has on others, so strong an impression of homogeneity that I believe that later alterations have not materially changed the general conception and purpose of the man whom I call 'the *Beowulf* poet'.

My task would be easier if it were possible to state categorically when and for whom the author was working; but both these are problematic matters, and it will be in place to begin with them. It will first be necessary to examine the attitude to the Christian faith of the audience the poet had in mind.

He was composing for Christians, whose conversion was neither partial nor superficial. He expects them to understand his allusions to biblical events without his troubling to be explicit about them. He does not think it necessary to tell them anything of the circumstances in which Cain slew Abel, or when, and why, 'the flood, the pouring ocean, slew the race of giants'.[1] He assumes their familiarity not merely with the biblical story, but with the interpretation in the commentaries —not, of course, necessarily at first hand, but through the teaching of the Church. His hearers would not have understood why it was 'the race of giants' that were destroyed by the flood, unless they were aware of the identification of the giants of Genesis vi. 4 ('There were giants in the earth in those days'), with the progeny of the union of the descendants of Seth with those of Cain, a union thought to be implied in Genesis vi. 2 ('The sons of God saw the daughters of men, that they were fair').[2] The passing reference earlier in the poem to 'giants, that fought against God for a long time; He paid them out for it'[3] would have been altogether cryptic and obscure to a newly converted audience. In fact, it is unlikely that a recently converted people would have known the word the poet uses for giants, for it is a Latin loan-word coming most probably from the Latin Bible, and the poet gives no explanatory gloss. It is not the only ecclesiastical Latin loan-word which

[1] ll. 1689 f.
[2] See O. F. Emerson, 'Legends of Cain, especially in Old and Middle English', *Pub. Mod. Lang. Assoc. Amer.* xxi (1906), 878–929.
[3] ll. 113 f.

he uses; *candel*, used only in a metaphorical sense, applied to the sun, *forscrifan*, a formation from the Latin *proscribere*, are other instances; and, most significant of all, as Professor Girvan has pointed out, the word *non* has had time to be generalized from its original application to a church service at the ninth hour till it indicates merely a certain time of the day. It is interesting to contrast the practice of the poet of the *Heliand* with that of the *Beowulf* poet in this respect, for while the latter says casually in a secular context 'Then came noon of the day'[1] the former normally glosses the term; for example, he says: 'the noon of the day at the ninth hour'[2] and 'at noon, when it was the ninth hour of the summer-long day'.[3] It is only when he uses the term for the third time that he allows it to stand unsupported. The poet of *Beowulf* expects the word to be understood; more than that, the context in which he uses it suggests that it no longer even had an ecclesiastical flavour.

It is quite true, as has frequently been commented on, that the biblical references are confined to Old Testament events. But it would be absurd to assume from that that the poet is composing for a partially converted audience who have been taught about Cain and Noah's flood, but have not yet got as far as the events of the New Testament. That is not how missionaries teach the faith of Christ. The missionaries to the Anglo-Saxons were not exceptional in this respect. They preached first of the major doctrines; they spoke of the Redemption of the world by Christ's Passion; the detailed

---

[1] l. 1600.   [2] *Heliand*, l. 3491.   [3] Ibid. ll. 3420 f.

stories of the Old Testament could be left till later, special emphasis being laid on such events as were held to foreshadow those of the New. When Benedict Biscop brought back from Rome pictures to adorn the churches of Wearmouth and Jarrow, with the express intent of influencing people who could not read, among those first chosen were pictures from the gospels and the Apocalypse; on a later visit he brought back a series to illustrate the connexion of the Old and the New Testament.[1] Any set of persons in Anglo-Saxon times that is well-informed on the Old Testament can be assumed to be cognizant of the Christian faith as a whole. The absence from our poem of allusions to the New Testament must receive some other explanation than one which supposes that such allusions would be unintelligible to an audience that knows about Cain and Abel. Nor is it difficult to provide another explanation; the theme which the poet has chosen, the ravages of monsters among mankind, leads him naturally to think of the giants of Genesis, and, indeed, forces him to find a place for his monsters in the scheme of Creation, as set out in Genesis. It is his theme, not his inclination, still less any doubt of his audience's knowledge of Christianity, that limits his allusions to Old Testament history.

An audience which understands biblical references will also be familiar with the stock metaphors of the homiletic tradition, themselves often of biblical origin.

[1] Bede, *Historia Abbatum*, ed. C. Plummer, *Baedae Opera Historica*, i. 369 f., 373.

The poet is not afraid of being misunderstood when he
speaks of 'the slayer . . . who shoots wickedly from his
bow'[1] or of the man who, when the 'guardian of the
soul' sleeps, 'is struck under his helmet with a sharp
arrow'.[2] The metaphors of the spiritual armour against
the arrows of the devil are too much the common
property of sermon literature for it to be worth while
to look for a specific source for their use in *Beowulf*.
They occur, for example, in Vercelli homily No. IV.[3]
The poet need not have been conscious of passages like
Ephesians vi. 16. What is important is that he regards
such metaphors as instantly intelligible to his hearers,
and this could not have been the position in the earliest
days after the conversion of the English.

It is in keeping with all this that the poet assumes that
the conception of a last judgement, of retribution after
death for sins, of eternal life for the righteous, will be
accepted without question. He does not labour these
matters; he does not need to; he is not asserting them
against a different point of view. His audience accept
the Christian dogmas and the poem is free from religious
polemic.

I would go further than claiming that the audience
of *Beowulf* was thoroughly acquainted with the Christian
religion. I believe that it was also accustomed to listen
to Christian poetry. There is no general difficulty in the
way of such an assumption, unless one wishes to date

[1] ll. 1743 f.   [2] ll. 1742, 1745 f.
[3] *Die Vercelli-Homilien*, ed. M. Förster (*Bibliothek der angelsächsischen
Prosa*, xii, Hamburg, 1932), pp. 103–6.

the poem very early indeed. Already when Bede was writing his *Historia Ecclesiastica*, which he tells us he finished in 731, there had been a number of poets who had followed Caedmon's example and composed religious poems in the traditional native metre;[1] and from *Beowulf* itself it can legitimately be gathered that it was not only ecclesiastics who listened to poems on religious themes. Whatever may have been the poet's reason for making Hrothgar's minstrel sing in Heorot of the Creation—a matter to which I shall return—the picture he draws would surely have been incongruous, or even ludicrous, if minstrels never sang on such themes to lay audiences. To depict the heathen retainers of a Danish king as listening to Christian poetry would have been impossible if such a procedure had been abnormal at the courts of the Christian kings of his own day.

It is not, however, simply on general probability that I am basing this claim. I have committed myself elsewhere[2] to the view that the poet did not himself invent all his poetic expressions for Christian conceptions, but drew them from a common store that had gradually grown up among poets dealing with religious subjects. I will elaborate a little on this opinion. The poet uses a great number of Christian expressions that are also to be found in surviving religious verse. This verse shares with *Beowulf* not only many of the poetic peri-phrases for the divinity, such as *wuldres wealdend, lif-frea*,

[1] Bede, *Historia Ecclesiastica*, book iv, chap. 22 (24), ed. Plummer, op. cit., p. 259.

[2] 'Anglo-Saxon Poetry and the Historian', *Trans. R. Hist. Soc.*, Fourth Series, xxxi (1949), 83.

wuldorcyning, sigora waldend, heofena helm, dæda demend, but many other expressions also: e.g. *miclan domes* 'of the great judgement', *werhðo dreogan* 'suffer damnation', *ece rædas* 'eternal benefits', *lænan lifes* 'of this transitory life'—all of them complete half-lines—, *God eaðe mæg* 'God can easily', always used as a second half-line with its object in the following line. Much of the verse in which these expressions occur is probably later than *Beowulf,* none can be proved to be earlier, for I consider the expression *ece Dryhten* 'eternal Lord', shared by *Beowulf* and Caedmon's Hymn, to be too obvious an epithet for the divinity for it to carry any weight in this argument. It would therefore be possible to claim that the other poets who use these expressions were borrowing them from *Beowulf.* But is it likely? It would indeed be odd if it first occurred to a poet whose theme is not primarily religious to invent so much new phraseology for Christian conceptions, sometimes apparently by translating expressions in the Vulgate or the early Christian hymns, and if subsequent poets, composing on religious themes, used this predominantly secular work as a store-house of Christian phrases. It is easier to imagine the *Beowulf* poet and these religious poets deriving the diction they have in common from the same source, earlier religious verse which has not survived.

That this is the true explanation is supported by the impression which some of the Christian phrases in *Beowulf* make, of not having been invented for their present context. For example, some expressions used of Grendel and the dragon are applied to the devil elsewhere, and this sometimes is their more original use. Some of them are, as Klaeber has shown,[1] translations of Latin periphrases for the devil, e.g. *captivus inferni* rendered as *helle hæfta*, *hostis antiquus* as *ealdgewinna*, *hostis humani generis* as *feond mancynnes*. Probably the audience was familiar with these descriptions of the archfiend and accustomed to hear them used in a more general sense to emphasize the evil malignity of other beings. The phrase 'to seek the concourse of devils'[2] does not sound as if it were first coined to describe Grendel's wish to reach the lair which he inhabits alone with his mother; and would the poet have gone out of his way to invent the periphrasis for death 'he chose God's light'[3] in order to describe the passing of a heathen king, however anxious he may be to ignore the heathenism of his characters? But if it were already a recognized poetic circumlocution for 'he died', the poet might well employ a ready-made half-line without thinking too much about its implications. Surely, however, he could do so only if his hearers were likely to understand it in the same weakened connotation as he did. If to them it were a new and unfamiliar expression, they would give it its full meaning, and might well have felt it incongruous. The poet is free to use Christian poetic phraseology somewhat inexactly if it has come to be an accepted convention. But whether it be conceded or not that the poet's first hearers were familiar with much of his Christian phraseology in a different kind of

---

[1] 'Die christlichen Elemente im Beowulf', *Anglia*, xxxv (1911–12), 249–59.   [2] l. 756.   [3] l. 2469.

setting, it seems clear enough that their religious education was too thorough for them to be recent converts.

It is not necessarily a sign of very early date that the
poet should expect his audience to be interested in the
vivid and impressive funeral rites of the heathen period,
and should therefore describe at length the ship-burial
of Scyld and the cremation of Beowulf. It would be a
different matter if it could be proved that these descriptions were based on eye-witness accounts. This matter
will have to be discussed more fully later on. Here I will
only say that as long as it is open to us to believe that these
descriptions were drawn from earlier accounts, in poetry
or otherwise, we need not date the poem within living
memory of these ceremonies. The poet may have found
similar scenes described in the sources from which not
only he, but his hearers also, had gained their knowledge of the heroic stories alluded to in the poem. I have
suggested elsewhere[1] that before so Christian a poet—
and here I would add so Christian an audience—can
take pleasure in detailed accounts of heathen burial
rites, those rites must be so far in the past as to have lost
much of their association with other, more obnoxious,
heathen ceremonies. As long as the fate of Christianity
in England was in any way insecure, its more pious
adherents could hardly enjoy hearing of the practices
of a heathenism from which they had only recently been
released, even if purely heathen poems were still being
listened to by their less religiously minded contemporaries.

[1] 'Anglo-Saxon Poetry and the Historian', op. cit., p. 83.

Neither is it a sign of early date that the audience is assumed to be interested in the blood-feud, to judge by the frequent references to stories which turn on this motive. If this implies a people not fully weaned from heathen ethics, the same could be said with equal justice of the Anglo-Saxons throughout their history. For the duty of protecting one's kindred, or one's lord, or one's man, and of exacting retribution from the slayer and his kindred if any of these were killed, was not superseded by Christianity. Action by the kindred, or, in special circumstances, by other persons empowered to act in their place, was the only means by which Anglo-Saxon law dealt with homicide until after the Norman Conquest. It is true that the Church threw the weight of its authority to support the practice of settling feuds by the payment of wergilds instead of by the actual taking of vengeance, and that the law tried to put some pressure on the offender to make him pay composition for his deed. But even if the combined efforts of Church and State had been completely effective, there would remain the problem of the poor man of a poor kindred, who could not pay the wergild. Was such a person to be allowed to kill with impunity? In such cases, and also when, as frequently happened, passions were too enraged for peaceful settlement to be acceptable, the vengeance was allowed to take its course. A few examples will show that killing for the sake of vengeance was not felt to be incompatible with Christian ethics at any period in Anglo-Saxon times.

In 801 no less prominent a churchman than Alcuin

himself wrote to Charles the Great in recommendation
of a Northumbrian nobleman called Torhtmund that
he had 'boldly avenged the blood of his lord'.[1] Towards
the end of the tenth century, the Cambridge Thanes'
Guild, an association of a semi-religious, semi-social
character, had its statutes entered on what was most
probably a fly-leaf of a gospel-book once belonging to
the monastery of Ely. These statutes pronounce: 'If any
guild-brother slays a man, and does so as an avenger by
necessity, and to remedy the insult to him . . . each
guild-brother is to supply half a mark to his aid. . . . If,
however, the guild-brother slay anyone foolishly and
wantonly, he is to be himself responsible for what he has
done.'[2] These men were loyal sons of the Church; they
rendered their alms to St. Audrey at Ely, they made
arrangements for due Christian ceremony at their
burial; but they recognized that any one of them might
find himself an avenger by necessity, and they saw
nothing blameworthy in such an act. So when the
Beowulf poet lets his hero speak those famous words:
'Better it is for each that he avenge his friend than
mourn much'[3]—in a situation, we may notice, where no
question of compensation could arise, since this type of
foe 'did not wish to remove the deadly enmity, to compound with money'[4]—it is no mere reminiscence of
heathen times, but a sentiment that all present could
applaud. Feeling could still run strong on this matter

[1] *Alcuini Epistolae*, ed. Dümmler (Mon. Germ. Hist., Epist. Karolini
Aevi, ii), p. 376.
[2] B. Thorpe, *Diplomatarium Anglicum Ævi Saxonici*, pp. 611 f.
[3] ll. 1384 f.   [4] ll. 154, 156.

even as late as the episcopate of Wulfstan II of Worcester (1062–95), when, we are told, the brothers of a slain man declared that they would rather be utterly (*omnino*) excommunicated than fail to avenge the death of their brother. On this occasion both ecclesiastical and popular opinion felt the attitude to be unreasonable, but this was because the slaying had been accidental and the slayer was willing to pay full reparation. Divine vengeance afflicted one brother with madness, and the others came to a better frame of mind.[1] The *Life of St. Wulfstan*, which records this incident, has another, slighter reference to the continuance of feuds at this time: a rich priest was set on by his foes and killed, and since he had been scornful of St. Wulfstan's advice, the biographer makes no adverse comment on this act of violence.[2] The first of these incidents took place in the diocese of Worcester and thus proves that it was not only in the Scandinavianized North and East of the country that the blood-feud was current in late Saxon times.

Beowulf's sage remark: 'Rarely anywhere does the slaughtering spear remain at rest even a little while after the fall of men',[3] was true not only in the days of an heroic past. One of the codes of King Edmund (939–46) attempted to curb the blood-feud,[4] and it reveals the tremendous care necessary to prevent the flaring up afresh of emotions while the feud was being

[1] *The Vita Wulfstani of William of Malmesbury*, ed. R. R. Darlington, pp. 38 f.

[2] Ibid., pp. 92 f.　　　　　　　　　　　[3] ll. 2029–31.

[4] II Edmund. See especially chaps. 7–7.3.

settled. The slayer and the kindred of the slain man must each have an advocate, and the slayer is not to approach in order to pledge himself to pay the wergild until the kin of the slain man have given security to his advocate that he may do so under safe-conduct. When this has been done and the slayer has found surety for the payment of the wergild, the king's *mund* is to be established, that is to say, any act of violence committed by either party will be regarded as a breach of the king's own right of affording protection, and make the offender liable to a very heavy fine, over and above the other consequences of his act. There is an interesting account of how in the eleventh century a feud broke out again after settlement, and, though it comes from a rather late source, there is no reason to reject its general accuracy.[1] When Earl Aldred of Northumbria had taken vengeance for his father's murder by killing the murderer, Thurbrand, there was a deadly feud between him and Carl, Thurbrand's son. But eventually, by the agency of friends, reparations were made and the feud was so completely settled that the two protagonists became sworn brothers. We are not told what renewed the quarrel, but it underlines my point—that it was not only men hostile or indifferent to the teachings of the Church who admitted the duty of vengeance—to note that Carl killed Aldred at the

[1] It is the tract known as 'De obsessione Dunelmi', in *Symeonis Monachi Opera Omnia*, ed. T. Arnold, *R.S.*, i (1882), pp. 215–20. It was written at Durham at the end of the eleventh century, and I suspect the author to be drawing on an oral narrative. Even if the details of the story cannot be vouched for, it still reveals how the blood-feud was regarded.

very moment when they were waiting for a favourable wind for them to start on a pilgrimage to Rome together. Aldred lay long unavenged, but in 1073 his grandson sent a band of assassins who took the sons and grandsons of Carl by surprise as they were feasting at Settrington, and slew all but one, whom they spared for his goodness of disposition. Aldred's grandson who organized this massacre was Earl Waltheof, who was regarded in some quarters as a martyr after his execution by William the Conqueror.

I think it is important, if we wish to estimate the effect of our poem on its contemporaries, to realize that there is no period in Anglo-Saxon history when the interest taken in the carrying out of vengeance would be merely antiquarian. The tales referred to in the poem would not be regarded simply as violent, dramatic tales of the bad old days, or, in nostalgic mood, the good old days. Like the thanes of the Cambridge Guild mentioned above, any man of the audience might find himself suddenly forced to become an avenger by necessity, perhaps in circumstances that involved his acting counter to his inclination and affections. The dilemma of an Ingeld or a Hengest might one day be his own. The poet's allusions to characters such as these give his poem more than an 'historical' background; they hint at a problem that was real to the poet's contemporaries.

Some years ago, I suggested that a puzzling passage in the poem became clear enough if one looked for its interpretation to Anglo-Saxon law instead of to remote

legends.[1] When the poet wishes to bring home to his
audience the utter desolation of the old King Hrethel
when one of his sons has been accidentally killed by
another, he compares his situation to that of a man
whose son is hanging on the gallows,[2] for it was a principle of Anglo-Saxon law that no vengeance could be
taken for an executed criminal, and Hrethel is just as
effectively cut off from the consolation of exacting a
great reparation or taking vengeance, though for very
different reasons. Similarly, the story of how Carl slew
Earl Aldred, which is certainly based on history, may
help us to understand how Hengest in the Finn story
could turn against Finn, in spite of his having accepted
a settlement with him. Like Carl, Hengest could not
refrain from brooding on his loss, even though he had
come to terms. Carl had accepted a wergild, and I
do not understand why Klaeber should pronounce so
categorically that in the Finn episode the gold brought
from the hoard after the oath was performed[3] could not
have been for the payment of wergild. It is difficult to
see how Hengest and his party could have come to
terms with Finn without a settlement being paid for
Hnæf.[4] We are not expressly told so, in this very summarized and selective account, but this is as likely to be
because it would have been so obvious in the poet's day
as because it did not take place. However, unless fresh

---

[1] *Medium Ævum*, viii. 198–204.   [2] ll. 2444–62.

[3] Keeping the manuscript reading *að* 'oath', instead of the common
emendation to *ad* 'pyre'.

[4] ll. 1107 f. Cf. Klaeber, p. 173: 'The payment of *wergild* seems out
of the question'.

evidence should come to light, we shall never reach certainty in interpreting this part of *Beowulf*, and too much brooding over our inadequate scraps of evidence for the Finn tale has been one of the most unprofitable and time-consuming occupations of *Beowulf* scholars.[1]

One may reach the conclusion that the audience of *Beowulf* was a Christian company, and one which admitted that vengeance, in unavoidable circumstances and carried out in accordance with the law, was a binding duty. This second consideration is of no help at all in our dating of the poem; but the first, its Christianity, is. The depth of its Christian knowledge is for this purpose far more important than that of the poet himself, for his Christian education might be exceptional; it would be unsafe to argue from it to the general conditions of his day. Nor would the extent of the audience's Christianity be of much assistance in dating the poem if there were any reason to suppose that the poet was addressing himself to ecclesiastics alone. My choice of the term 'audience' has already indicated that I do not believe that *Beowulf* was composed merely for people who could read, which is almost equivalent to saying, for the clergy. Nothing that is recorded of the ecclesiastics of Anglo-Saxon England lends countenance to a view that they were in the habit of composing long poems on secular themes solely for circulation among themselves. It is difficult to imagine any bishop or abbot approving the use of so much expensive parchment for

[1] Cf. review of Chambers, *Beowulf: An Introduction*, 1st edit., in *T.L.S.* (12 Jan. 1922), p. 26 (by Bruce Dickins).

a work which he would not regard as directly edifying
to men of religion. Some of these were interested in the
tales of the Germanic heroes, and scandalized Alcuin
in 797, but nothing in the letter in which he reproved
the monks of Lindisfarne for their interest in songs about
Ingeld[1] suggests that this taste was pandered to in
monastic scriptoria. *Beowulf*, though it may contain
elements intended for edification, is surely first and foremost literature of entertainment, and as such, intended
mainly for laymen. The scholarly tastes of King Aldfrith of Northumbria should not lead us to suppose that
literacy was very common among the upper classes of
the laity. Aldfrith, an illegitimate son who had spent
his youth in exile in Celtic lands, with little hope of
succeeding to the throne or to high preferment at home,
received an education that was certainly not typical
among men of rank. It would be hazardous to postulate
a considerable reading public of laymen, and I do not
consider the length of *Beowulf* an insuperable obstacle
to the view that it was intended for oral recital. It could
easily have been delivered in three sittings. It is perhaps
not by accident that the second episode, the fight with
Grendel's mother, begins with a neat synopsis of what
has gone before;[2] this may be intended to inform new-
comers and remind the previous audience of what has
happened in the first part. The third episode, the
dragon fight, is intelligible by itself. The ease with
which the work divides in this way does not force us
to suppose that it was intended for oral performance,

[1] *Alcuini Epistolae*, p. 183.   [2] ll. 1251–76.

but it supports such a view if this is probable on other grounds.

For a lay company to be so steeped in Christian doctrines, a considerable time must have elapsed since the acceptance of Christianity. This is still more certain if the terminology of Christian vernacular poetry has become so familiar that it can be used in a generalized and weakened sense; for, if we are to believe Bede, it was not until late in the seventh century that the native poetic technique was first applied to religious subjects. One must allow no short time for the spread of this habit till the point is reached when a poet could take for granted his audience's familiarity with the conventions of Christian poetry. But even apart from this considera-tion, it is doubtful whether the attitude to Christianity and the knowledge of it, which are implied by the poem, could be as early as the seventh century, and perhaps not even early in the eighth. The spread of the new faith was not so rapid as all that. A hundred years after Augustine's landing, a king of Kent finds it necessary to legislate against the worship of 'devils',[1] and about the same period there are parts of England in which Christianity had only recently been accepted as an official religion.[2] Bede, writing in 734, is of the opinion that the Church in Northumbria is far too understaffed for effective instruction in the Christian faith to be given to the laity throughout the kingdom. If, then, it is

[1] Wihtred, chaps. 12 f.
[2] The conversion of Sussex dates from 680, that of the Isle of Wight from 686.

desired to date *Beowulf* in Bede's lifetime, it must be assumed that it was intended for a section of the community with a degree of religious education far above that of the average layman; or, alternatively, that it was composed outside Northumbria, and that this kingdom was worse off than other parts of England in this matter of religious education. If this were so, one would have to attribute this backwardness to the particular difficulties of communication in this kingdom, and perhaps also to Wilfrid's long resistance to the subdivision of his see; but all our available evidence suggests that Northumbria in the eighth century was in advance of other kingdoms, many of which had been converted later, and not behind them.

In view of these difficulties, it might be as well to consider if we really are forced to date *Beowulf* in the age of Bede (*c.* 672–735). Of late years, it seems to have become widely accepted as a dogma that that is where the poem must be placed. For example, Berendsohn works on the assumption that it was written by an Anglian poet about 700,[1] while a Swedish archaeologist wrote in 1948: 'It is generally accepted that *Beowulf* was composed in about A.D. 700, that is to say, while many of those who had witnessed the burial at Sutton Hoo were still alive.'[2] The question whether some of the poet's audience could have seen ceremonies of this kind is one to which we must return. But this quotation shows

[1] W. A. Berendsohn, *Zur Vorgeschichte des 'Beowulf'* (Copenhagen, 1935), p. 233.

[2] Sune Lindqvist, 'Sutton Hoo and Beowulf', *Antiquity*, xxii. 131.

that so confident a dating, if there are no strong grounds for it, may be misleading a scholar in another field, and causing him to draw some false conclusions. The interests of scholars other than those whose primary concern is with *Beowulf* may therefore be served by a re-examination of the evidence for dating the poem.

There have been many advocates for a date in 'the age of Bede'. To quote only more recent writers, Lawrence wrote in 1928: 'The commonly accepted dating in the age of Bede remains unshaken'[1] and Professor Tolkien said in 1936: 'I accept without argument throughout the attribution of *Beowulf* to the "age of Bede"—one of the firmer conclusions of a department of research most clearly serviceable to criticism: inquiry into the probable date of the effective composition of the poem as we have it.'[2] Chambers in 1932, though still clinging to 'the age of Bede', seemed willing to interpret this somewhat widely, to cover a period from 650 to 750.[3] Crawford wrote in 1931: 'There is a general consensus of opinion that *Beowulf* was written about the middle of the eighth century',[4] a date a little late for the age of Bede, if we take that literally. Klaeber favoured in 1922 a date in the first half of the eighth century, 'perhaps not far from the middle of it'.[5] In the third edition of his work (1936), he cut out this last remark. The claim of the more recent writers mentioned

---

[1] W. W. Lawrence, *Beowulf and Epic Tradition*, p. 263.
[2] J. R. R. Tolkien, 'Beowulf: the Monsters and the Critics', *Proc. Brit. Acad.* xxii. 262.
[3] Chambers, p. 393.   [4] 'Beowulfiana', *Rev. Eng. Stud.* vii. 448.
[5] *Beowulf and the Fight at Finnsburg*, 1st edit., p. cxvi.

above to a general acceptance of a date about 700, is no doubt to be attributed to Professor Girvan's *Beowulf and the Seventh Century*, which was published in 1935; but, though this work argues convincingly that the poem is not earlier than the late seventh century, the evidence brought forward does not, in my opinion, prove that it is not later than this time. Finally, Schücking has never, to my knowledge, retracted his view that the poem belongs to about 900,[1] and, though he has won little support in England, recent correspondence and conversation with German scholars has shown me that some are still inclined to regard so late a date as a possibility with which one must reckon.

So late a date seems highly unlikely. The poem is surely pre-Viking Age. It may be true that we should not attach an exaggerated importance to the high terms of praise and respect with which the poet speaks of the Danes and their rulers. Heroic poetry shows respect to kings and chieftains as such; the poet would probably have used similar terms of the Goths, the Lombards, or the Burgundians, or any other nation, if the story he was telling had happened to be located in their courts. It is not in order to pay honour to the Danes, but to heighten the dignity of his subject, that the poet lays such stress on the might and splendour of the court where his monsters' ravages take place. All this I would readily yield. Yet, I doubt whether he would have spoken in these terms during the Viking

[1] 'Wann entstand der Beowulf? Glossen, Zweifel und Fragen', *Beitr. zur Gesch. d. deut. Spr.* xlii (1917), 347–410.

Age, or whether his audience would have given him a patient hearing if he had. It is not how men like to hear the people described who are burning their homes, pillaging their churches, ravaging their cattle and crops, killing their countrymen or carrying them off into slavery. So, if the poem is later than the time when Viking invasions began in earnest, about 835, it can hardly be placed before the tenth century, and even then it would have to be put, as Schücking puts it, in the court of an Anglo-Danish king in the Danelaw. It could hardly be located in English England until the reign of Cnut, and that is later than our surviving manuscript.

When Schücking defends his late dating of the poem, he makes several penetrating observations about the advanced civilization portrayed in the poem which deserve general acceptance; but I do not understand why he should disallow such a civilization to the England of the days of Boniface or of Alcuin. There is certainly no sign that the Danelaw of the petty Scandinavian kings, Eohric, Siefred, Rægnold, Sihtric, the two Anlafs, Eric Blood-Axe, &c., was a more civilized land than England in the eighth century. There is also a linguistic difficulty about attributing *Beowulf* to their courts: these men spoke Norse. Schücking gets round these difficulties by his suggestion that an English poet was commissioned by a Danelaw prince to produce the poem for the education of his sons. I should be sorry to believe that the poem was from the beginning what it has since too often become, a work studied by young people to whom the language is unfamiliar, and it would need positive evidence of a late date to force this conception on me. Beyond the respect paid to the Danes, which can be accounted for otherwise, there seems to be none. Alcuin's reference to Ingeld shows that one Scandinavian story, at any rate, was popular in eighth-century England, so it cannot be argued that the interest in Scandinavian tales began with the Danish settlement. Linguistically and metrically the poem differs from datable tenth-century poems, and the proper names show no influence of the forms that would be in use in Scandinavian versions of these tales in the Viking Age and later. For example, it does not use *Sconeg*, as Alfred does, but retains *Scedenig*. The tone of the poem's Christianity does not suggest a period when the Church was fighting the fresh wave of heathenism introduced by the Danish and Norwegian settlers, and the Christian knowledge the poet assumes in his audience would not be possessed by the followers of the recently and imperfectly converted monarchs of the Danelaw.

Though I cannot concur in so late a date for our poem, I think it desirable to reconsider the evidence on which so many scholars put their final limit about 750. Why do they so firmly exclude the second half of the eighth century? The evidence they depend on is partly linguistic, partly historical. Metre shows that the poem contained some early linguistic features which do not occur in the poetry of Cynewulf and his school. But there is very little contemporary evidence to help us to put an absolute date to the sound changes involved, and even the arranging of the various poems in a relative chronology is completely valid only if there is reason to suppose that they come from approximately the same part of the country. The rate of development need not have been uniform in the various dialects. The most definite of the early linguistic features is the presence, proved by metre, of uncontracted forms, mainly where later contracted forms arose from the loss of an intervocalic *h*.[1] How unsafe it would be to date *Beowulf* about 700 for this reason is shown by the presence of *Guthlac A* in Professor Girvan's list of poems in which a similar condition is found, for this poem is almost certainly based on Felix's Latin *Life of St. Guthlac*, for which 730 seems about the earliest likely date. In glosses, which are assumed (by no means certainly) to go back to an original of about 680–720, the intervocalic *h* is sometimes still preserved. A Kentish charter of 679 affords an instance of its loss, but this occurs in the second element of a compound place-name, and not in stressed position.[2] It has not hitherto been noticed in this connexion that a questionable charter from Malmesbury Abbey, which nevertheless contains a genuine list of witnesses of 705–9,[3] has in this list the name *Haeha* for an abbot whom later sources, mistaking the oblique case for the nominative, refer to as *Hean*; and, if the *h* could be preserved as late as the beginning

[1] See e.g. R. Girvan, *Beowulf and the Seventh Century* (Methuen's Old English Library, 1935), pp. 16–18; Klaeber, 3rd edit., pp. cviii–cx; Chambers, p. 111.

[2] *Brit. Mus. Facs*. i. Pl. 1; Birch, *Cartularium Saxonicum*, i, No. 45.

[3] See H. M. Chadwick, *Studies on Anglo-Saxon Institutions* (Cambridge, 1905), p. 286; F. M. Stenton, *The Early History of the Abbey of Abingdon* (Reading, 1913), pp. 16 f.

of the eighth century, it would be rash to assume that its loss, and the later development by which the resulting hiatus was got rid of by contraction, were all over and done with so long before the second half of the eighth century that even poetry—archaic and conservative as this so frequently is—could not avail itself of the dissyllabic forms after about 750.[1] I suspect that the belief that linguistic evidence forbids a later date than 750 for *Beowulf* is to a great extent based on too early a dating of the work of Cynewulf, and that scholars have been slow to realize that, when Dr. Sisam showed that no valid reason prevents our assigning Cynewulf's work to the ninth century,[2] he was also giving us a much longer manœuvring space in relation to *Beowulf*.

As for historical reasons for fixing the date of the poem, I have tried elsewhere[3] to indicate that it is not enough to show, however convincingly, that the poem fits into a certain historical context, unless one can also show that no other historical context exists into which it could equally well be fitted; and, as our evidence is fragmentary and unequally distributed, there may well have been contexts about which we know little or nothing which would have suited our requirements very well. The fullness of the records for the age of Bede has made it possible for a case to be made out for

[1] See also the recent article by R. Quirk in *Mod. Lang. Rev.* xlv (1950), 1–5.

[2] K. Sisam, 'Cynewulf and his Poetry', *Proc. Brit. Acad.* xviii (1932), 304–8.

[3] D. Whitelock, 'Anglo-Saxon Poetry and the Historian', op. cit., pp. 78, 85–8.

the court of Aldfrith of Northumbria (685–705) as the place where *Beowulf* was first produced;[1] but enough is known about Eadberht Eating, king of Northumbria from 737 to 758, to show that he could have sponsored such a poem, while quite a number of rulers about whom, by accident, less is known may be eligible for the position of patron to our poet. On historic grounds alone, one could not reject the great Mercian kings, Æthelbald and Offa, or Ælfwald of East Anglia, to whom Felix dedicated his *Life of St. Guthlac*, or Alhred and Ælfwald of Northumbria, or Ine and Cynewulf of Wessex, or various Kentish kings. One can sympathize with a desire to assign *Beowulf* to the age of Bede, and thus make it contemporary with the masterpieces of Northumbrian art, such as the best Anglian crosses and the Lindisfarne Gospels; and I should like to make it clear that I do not wish to argue that the poem *could* not have been composed then, but merely that it *need* not have been. It is not that I wish to substitute a different date from that so commonly held, but rather to extend the later limit to include the later eighth century within the range of possibility, because I believe that the interests of Beowulfian scholarship will be best served by a refusal to settle securely into too definite a dating at present. The age of Bede may seem to supply so suitable a background to the poem merely by the accidental circumstance that it happens to be a period that is well recorded. Later on, I would like to

---

[1] A. S. Cook, 'The Possible Begetter of the O.E. Beowulf and Widsith', *Trans. of the Connecticut Academy of Arts and Science*, xxv. 281–346.

bring forward some evidence to suggest that the re-
mainder of the eighth century was not as unsuitable for
the production of a work of art of this scale as is sometimes supposed. First, however, we must see whether
the inquiry can be limited by establishing the area in
which *Beowulf* was composed.

It is normally accepted as dogma that the poet was
an Anglian, but opinions differ as to whether he belonged to the Mercian or Northumbrian branch of that
people. Like most Old English poetry, the poem contains in its present form some Anglian forms, and some
that are held to be specifically Mercian; but these forms
are not proved to go back to the poet himself by their
occurrence in rhyme, as are some of the Anglian forms
in Cynewulf's poetry.[1] There has of late been some
restiveness against the assumption that Anglian forms
in our extant manuscripts always, of necessity, indicate
that the authors were of Anglian origin, an assumption
which robs Wessex of poetry almost altogether, though
there is plenty of evidence for its cultivation there.
Doubt is most clearly expressed by Dr. Sisam, who says:
'A consideration of dialect conventions in Greek literature must raise doubts.' He points out also that 'without
early Southern texts, there is no sure distinction between
words, forms, and constructions unknown to Southern
poets in early times, and those, once general, that survived in Anglian only'.[2] Professor Girvan has suggested

---

[1] K. Sisam, op. cit., p. 304.
[2] Review of Menner, 'The Poetical Dialogues of Salomon and Saturn',
in *Medium Ævum*, xiii. 32.

that the Northumbrian origin of the earliest vernacular Christian poetry may have given Anglian forms a prestige, and caused them to be used by poets of other areas.[1] Chambers also felt dubious about establishing the locality of the poem solely on linguistic grounds, and repeated Sedgefield's argument that the same scriptorium could contain men from various areas, which might lead to some dialect admixture.[2] We may note that Peterborough has been shown to possess daughter houses in the eighth century in places as far apart as Breedon in Leicestershire, Woking and Bermondsey in Surrey, Hoo in Kent, and perhaps Brixworth in Northamptonshire.[3] Nor was it only ecclesiastics who moved from kingdom to kingdom. It was common for men to take service under alien lords, and youths were sometimes brought up, as fosterlings or hostages, at courts outside their native kingdom. Minstrels were a peripatetic class. One could not even be certain that the *Beowulf* poet composed his poem for men of his own kingdom. What swayed Chambers more than the dialect forms in his location of the poem was the introduction of Offa, a king in ancient Angel, as the only 'English' character of the poem. How far this is a valid argument for Anglian provenance is a matter to which we shall have to return.

[1] *Beowulf and the Seventh Century*, pp. 13 f.
[2] Chambers, pp. 104 f. Compare *Beowulf*, ed. W. J. Sedgefield (Manchester, 1910), pp. 4 f.
[3] F. M. Stenton, 'Medeshamstede and its Colonies' in *Historical Essays in Honour of James Tait* (Manchester, 1933); id., *Anglo-Saxon England* (Oxford, 1943), p. 160.

Meanwhile, one must reckon with another possibility when assessing the significance of the Anglian forms in our manuscript. Sir Frank Stenton's work has made it clear how real and important was the authority wielded by the overlord of all the lands south of the Humber, the supremacy of which carried with it, according to a ninth-century authority, the title of *Bretwalda*. Sir Frank says: 'Before the end of the seventh century the overlord was dealing with his subject kings very much as he dealt with the hereditary nobility of his own country. His safe-conduct ran throughout their lands and he could transfer provinces from one of them to another. It was always wise for an under-king to obtain the overlord's consent to important grants of land.'[1] The overlord took tribute, and he required subject kings to attend his court and to fight under him in time of war, along with their following. From about 730 until 796, under two successive powerful kings, Æthelbald and Offa, this supremacy was held by Mercia, and the power of the overlord steadily increased. Offa treats with Charles the Great as if empowered to speak for the whole country. To Alcuin, writing to Offa, the whole of England is covered by the terms 'my country' (Northumbria) and 'your country' (the rest of England). The papal legates in 786 met a southern gathering convened by Offa, at which the West Saxon king Cynewulf was present, and a northern council. They clearly saw no necessity to consult any other rulers. Offa held councils

[1] Op. cit., p. 35; cf. 'The Supremacy of the Mercian Kings', *Eng. Hist. Rev.* xxxiii. 433–52.

attended by all the episcopate of southern England, but by Mercian laymen alone. He interfered in the affairs of other southern English kingdoms. Can we then be so certain, in view of all the evidence for Mercian influence and prestige, that the presence of Anglian linguistic forms in our poetic texts proves that the authors were Anglians? Is it not possible that the Mercian official language during the heyday of Mercian power was influential outside the area in which it was spoken? There is evidence of 'Mercian' forms in West Saxon before the time of Alfred's Mercian helpers.[1] Even if this possibility is rejected, there remains the likelihood that many works would be copied in Mercia during these days of its prosperity, and hence be available to subsequent copyists in an Anglian spelling.

It may be as well, therefore, to leave the question of original provenance just as open as that of exact date, even though this will put us to the trouble of looking for evidence of conditions in all the kingdoms of the Heptarchy. It is not that I have an axe to grind; I am not leading up to a suggestion that St. Aldhelm was the author of *Beowulf*, for example; but, if anyone were to put forward such a suggestion (and there have been wilder), it could not in my opinion be refuted on linguistic grounds alone.

[1] See Birch, *Cartularium Saxonicum*, i, No. 225, a charter of Cynewulf, dated 778 (*Brit. Mus. Facs.* ii, Pl. 3), and ii, No. 451, a charter of Æthelwulf, relating to lands in Devonshire, dated 847 (*Brit. Mus. Facs.* ii, Pl. 30).

II

THE main theme of the poem can be briefly stated. It is the story of a Geatish hero, Beowulf by name, who killed two supernatural beings that ravaged the court of a Danish king of the Scylding dynasty; who later, in his old age, after a long and successful reign, was fatally wounded by a dragon which was attacking his own people, the Geats, though he was successful in killing the dragon with the aid of a young kinsman called Wiglaf. In addition to the main theme, the poem is full of allusions of lesser or greater length to other stories, and two series of events in particular are referred to so frequently that it is obvious that the poet wishes them to be present in his hearers' thoughts as he tells his tale. The tragic stories of family strife within the Scylding dynasty, and of the wars fought by the kings of the Geats against the Swedes or the Franks, attain almost to the position of sub-plots to the two parts of *Beowulf* respectively. But this effect would be achieved only if the audience was already familiar with the stories concerned. At least, this is true of the Scylding feud. An ignorant audience might not only fail to see the bearing of the several detached allusions, but might well fail to connect them with one another, separated as they are by stretches of text dealing with other matters. A well-informed audience would call to mind the whole tale at each reference to it. The poet indicates that it is as well for a young prince to be generous before he

needs to be;[1] the audience may remember that the
Scylding prince Hrethric earned the nickname 'the
niggard with rings'—and did he not come to a sad end?
The poet describes how Hrothgar built a hall 'greater
than the sons of men had ever heard of', and hints at
its tragic end;[2] he expects his audience to know that it
was destined to see Hrothgar's strife with his own son-
in-law, and at last to perish in flames in a war between
kinsfolk that put an end to the Scylding dynasty. At the
time of the monster's ravages the members of that
dynasty 'by no means performed deeds of treachery,
at that time';[3] on the contrary, they and their followers
sat and listened with interest to a minstrel's lay of a feud
between kinsmen, in happy ignorance that before long
their own gracious queen, Wealhtheow, would, like the
Hildeburh in the lay, awake one morning 'to learn of
the slaughter of kinsmen',[4] would lose her son by a
kinsman's hand. The Scyldings were unaware of this
disaster in store, but the poet meant his audience to
remember it. Why else, after telling the tale of Finn with
such a particular emphasis on the situation of Hildeburh, should he have immediately followed the lay with
a pointed reminder that peace did not reign in the
Danish court for ever,[5] and then, on top of that, allow
Wealhtheow to hold the centre of the stage for a considerable portion of the poem, with her expressions of
confidence in the loyalty of the very nephew who was
to kill her son, and of gratification at the ideal unity

[1] ll. 20–5.   [2] ll. 69 f., 81–5.   [3] ll. 1018 f.
[4] Cf. ll. 1077–9.   [5] ll. 1164 f.

prevailing in the Danish court?[1] The poet was indeed
lucky if he achieved such a dramatic juxtaposition by
accident, and not by design. To an audience that did
not know that Hrothulf killed Hrethric, the whole
section would be pointless; but an audience that did
know, knew also that Hrethric did not lie unavenged.
So, towards the end of the first part of the poem, after
the poet has indicated how Hrothgar's attempt to settle
the ancient feud between the Danes and the Heathobards by a political marriage was foredoomed to failure,[2]
he has only to mention Heoroweard's name—and he
goes out of his way to do so[3]—and the whole of the final
act of the Scylding drama would leap into his audience's
minds, one of the most famous events in northern story,
which gave rise to the Old Norse poem, the *Bjarkamál*,
namely the slaying of Hrothulf by his cousin Heoroweard, in spite of a magnificent stand made by his
followers. The poet can now turn to another scene; he has
rounded off his picture of the Danish court just as effectively as if he had expatiated on the subsequent history
of its members—always provided that he can count
on the co-operation of his audience, for it has had to
supply most of the picture itself, from his hints.

One has to draw on Scandinavian evidence for the
events of the story as I have given them: for Hrethric's
nickname,[4] for his slaying by Hrothulf,[5] for Hrothulf's

---

[1] ll. 1168–1231.   [2] ll. 2020–69.   [3] ll. 2158–62.

[4] *Hnauggvanbaugi* in *Langfeðgatal*, ed. Langebek, *Scriptores Rerum Danicarum*, i. 5.

[5] *Saxonis Gesta Danorum*, ed. J. Olrik and H. Ræder (Copenhagen, 1931),
i. 56–7.

own death at Heoroweard's hands.[1] For it is clear that a story identical in its main outlines with what we can learn from the Scandinavian sources, much later though these are, must have been familiar to the poet's hearers. It is unlikely that they would have been content to derive merely a vague atmosphere of impending disaster from the allusions. People like to understand what they are told; in fact, many a story has been given a new turn in the telling by an attempt to explain a feature which has for some reason become obscure. Unless the poet could count on his audience's previous knowledge, not only would much of what he had to say have lost all significance, but he would surely have been running the risk of interruption. Someone might have dared to ask: 'What deeds of treachery did the Scyldings perform, and when?' or: 'What was all the fuss at Finnsburg about?' But I need not labour this point, for *Widsith* shows us that some tale of strife between Hrothgar and his nephew Hrothulf was known outside *Beowulf*,[2] while the popularity of the Ingeld story is proved not only by the reference in *Widsith*, but by Alcuin's famous query in his letter of 797 to the monks of Lindisfarne: 'What has Ingeld to do with Christ?'[3] Of the Finn story a fragment of a poetic version has survived, while the eponymous ancestor of the Scyldings, and his son, were inserted into the genealogy of the

[1] Ibid., pp. 51–62. *Hrólfs Saga Kraka*, chaps. 32–4, ed. Finnur Jónsson (1904), pp. 95–107; translation by S. M. Mills, *The Saga of Hrolf Kraki* (Oxford, 1933), pp. 77–88.

[2] *Widsith*, ll. 45–9.

[3] 'Quid Hinieldus cum Christo?' See p. 20, note 1 above.

West Saxon royal house, and a tenth-century member of this house, the chronicler Æthelweard, was familiar with the story of a child's mysterious arrival across the sea which is hinted at in *Beowulf*, though he allots it to Scyld's father, Scef, not, as does the poet, to Scyld himself.[1] Heremod, another Danish king whose story is obscurely alluded to in the poem,[2] occurs in the same genealogy. Some of these stories were current even after the Norman Conquest, as is shown by the occurrence of the names Rudolphus (Hrothulf) and Hunlapus (Hunlaf) along with those of other early heroes in the list, in Cotton MS. Vespasian D. IV, first discovered by Imelmann.[3] Some scholars would go farther than I have done in drawing details from Scandinavian sources to elucidate the allusions to the Scylding feud found in *Beowulf*; almost all agree with me so far.

More detailed consideration must be given to the problem of what the audience already knew about the kings of the Geats and their wars. There is no reference to these kings in *Widsith* or in any other extant poem. The only one of them who is known outside *Beowulf* is Hygelac, and references to him are not in poetry, but in works of a different kind. These references have a peculiar importance for *Beowulf* studies. This has been appreciated from the earliest days of serious work on the poem, for it was as early as 1815 that Grundtvig

[1] *Chronicon* of Æthelweard, ed. H. Savile, *Rerum Anglicarum Scriptores post Bedam*, p. 842; ed. H. Petrie, *Monumenta Historica Britannica*, i. 512.

[2] ll. 898–915, 1709–22.

[3] *Deut. Lit. Zeit.* xxx (1909), 999. See R. W. Chambers, *Widsith*, p. 254.

made what Chambers has called 'the most important discovery ever made in the study of *Beowulf*',[1] namely, that the Hygelac of the poem occurs in the writings of Frankish historians. Apart from Eormenric, a Gothic king to be identified with the Ermenrichus of Ammianus Marcellinus,[2] Hygelac is the only person mentioned in the poem whose existence can be proved from almost contemporary historical sources; and, while Eormenric receives a passing mention only,[3] Hygelac has a considerable part to play. The mere fact that one of the incidents in which he appears can be shown to be historical creates the probability that the other deeds ascribed to him and those of other Scandinavian kings may have a basis of fact. Hence it has become habitual to refer to those sections of the poem which contain no element of the marvellous as 'the historical element'. The passages from Frankish historians which contain the parallels to *Beowulf* have therefore been set out and considered again and again.[4] Nevertheless, they will stand some further discussion.

The account of Hygelac's ill-fated raid on the Rhineland is referred to four times in *Beowulf*, three times in the second half of the poem along with accounts of other wars fought by the kings of the Geats, and once isolated in a different type of context in the first part of the poem. When these various passages are put together, we get a story very close to one related by Gregory of

[1] Chambers, p. 4.

[2] *Rerum gestarum libri qui supersunt*, xxxi. 3, 1–2; ed. C. U. Clark, ii (Berlin, 1915), 562.   [3] ll. 1200 f.

[4] See, e.g., K. Malone, *Eng. Studies*, xxi (1939), 108–19.

Tours in his *History of the Franks*, in a part of his work which he finished in 575. He tells how a certain King Chlochilaichus and a Danish fleet raided Gaul and ravaged one region of Theuderic's kingdom, and, having loaded their ships with captives and other spoils, were about to return home when a strong force under the leadership of the king's son Theudebert came on the scene. Chlochilaichus had remained on shore, intending to follow later, and he was killed. His fleet was defeated in a great sea-battle, and all the booty recovered.[1] Gregory dates this occurrence somewhat vaguely, as after the events of the preceding chapter of his work, which deals with the consecration of Quintianus to the see of Clermont in 515. I doubt whether he could have given a precise date, for it has been shown that the raid probably took place between 520 and 531,[2] so that Gregory is writing more than forty years later.

Gregory's *History of the Franks* was known in England in the eighth century; it was used by Bede. It could have been known to the poet of *Beowulf*. Unless therefore we can prove that it was unlikely that he drew his account of Hygelac's raid from the Frankish historians, we must be cautious how we draw conclusions about the accuracy of oral tradition from the agreement between the poem and the Frankish sources. The English and Frankish accounts must first be shown to be independent of one another before such conclusions have any validity.

---

[1] Gregory of Tours, *Historia Francorum*, Book III, chap. 3.
[2] On the problem of the date, see Chambers, pp. 381–7.

35413

First, then, one must see if the poet's account contains any authentic information which he could not have derived from Frankish histories. It is easy to show that Gregory's account, in the form in which extant manuscripts of that work have it, could not have been the poet's sole source of information; he knows that a tribe called the Hetware were prominent among Hygelac's adversaries, and he did not invent this addition, for a later Frankish history, the *Liber Historiae Francorum*, sometimes called the *Gesta Francorum*, tells us that the district raided was that of the Attoarii, that is, the Hetware.[1] This work was first produced in 727. Again, it is possible that the poet had seen this history, if we do not wish to date *Beowulf* early in that century, possible, but not very likely. The poet's account has some variations from both Frankish sources. Some, such as the slaying of Dæghrefn, champion of the Franks (*Hugas*), by Beowulf, and the feat of swimming by which the latter reached his native land,[2] may be the poet's invention. It is true that Dæghrefn is a possible Frankish name, but anyone inventing the episode might wish to give a Frankish name to a Frankish character. The poet's statement that Hygelac's body and equipment passed into the keeping of the enemy could be his surmise from the Frankish accounts, which make it clear that his routed forces were not in a position to bear home their lord's body. One would not gather from the poem that the more important engagement was a

---

[1] Ed. B. Krusch, Mon. Germ. Hist., *Scriptores rerum Merovingicarum*, ii. 274.   [2] ll. 2501–8, 2359–68.

sea-battle, but the poet may have had his own reasons for concentrating on the fight on land in which the king was slain. The one important variation between the different accounts is that, to the poet, Hygelac is a king of the Geats, while the Frankish writers regard him as king of the Danes; for here it is highly probable that the poet is right and the Frankish sources wrong. It is at any rate easier to explain the substitution of the better known Danes for the remoter people the Geats than to account for the reverse process, and to attribute error to the poet in this particular would involve our rejecting all his other information concerning Hygelac and his line. It is no longer possible to show that the poet was right in regard to Hygelac's nationality and to the fate of his body by calling in the support of another work which refers to Hygelac, namely the *Liber Monstrorum*, for, as we shall see shortly, good reasons have been brought forward to show that this is not a Frankish but an English work; its evidence and that of the poem need not be independent of one another.

There is, however, another line of approach to the question: Did the poet use the Frankish histories? It turns on this: Is the poet informing his audience of something which is new to it, or is he, once again, reminding it of something which it knows already? If the latter alternative is the true one, then a written source for his information is improbable. To assume it would necessitate our confining the public to whom the work is addressed to a small circle of scholars learned in Frankish history.

The first reference in the poem to the raid would surely have seemed a little abrupt and over-compressed to anyone hearing of Hygelac's Rhineland raid for the first time. Let us consider the context and the passage.[1] Queen Wealhtheow has just given Beowulf a magnificent necklace—probably what archaeologists call a torque—one that lent itself for comparison with a necklace, the *Brosinga mene*, far famed in story. The poet then tells of the subsequent fate of that treasure, either to stress still further its surpassing value, by showing that it was chosen as a fit adornment for a king bent on a great exploit, or else to indicate how short-lived is earthly success, when the hero's splendid reward for his valour passed so rapidly into an enemy's possession. The poet says:

Hygelac of the Geats, nephew of Swerting, had that torque on his last journey, when he defended treasure under his standard, protected his spoils. Fate carried him off when out of pride he courted disaster, hostility against the Frisians. He bore that ornament, those precious stones, across the cup of the waves, that powerful prince. He fell under his shield. The body of the king, his breast-armour and the torque as well, passed into the possession of the Frankish king; inferior warriors robbed the slain after the carnage of the Geatish people, and held the place of corpses.[2]

This is, of course, more than a passing allusion, but would not anyone without previous knowledge of the incident have wanted to know what booty Hygelac was

[1] ll. 1192–1214.
[2] Or 'inferior warriors robbed the slain after the carnage; the people of the Geats held (i.e. covered) the place of corpses'.

defending? Moreover, if the poet is relating something that the audience does not know, then he expects it to remember this passage when, eleven hundred and forty lines farther on, he chooses to refer again to this event. It is in this second reference that he mentions casually that the opponents were Hetware, but he is here mainly concerned with his hero's prowess in the fight, and his escape by swimming.[1] The third reference to the raid is still more allusive: Beowulf, without specifying the occasion, is made to tell how he killed Dæghrefn, champion of the Franks (*Hugas*), and thus prevented him from delivering the breast-adornment to the Frisian king.[2] It is not until his last reference that the poet speaks in clear terms of a raiding fleet brought by Hygelac into the land of the Frisians and of a superior force of the Hetware which defeated and killed him. Never afterwards, we are told, was the favour of the Merovingian granted to the Geats.[3] Once again the impression is given that, if the audience was not confused by this method of narration, it was because it was hearing of familiar things.

If so, and if, as seems almost certain, the audience had obtained its knowledge from oral traditions, are we entitled to regard *Beowulf* as completely independent of Frankish versions of the story, and so to take the remarkably close agreement between it and the Frankish historians as a striking example of the reliability of oral tradition over a long period? I should like to think so, but I am not certain that we are justified in so doing.

[1] ll. 2354–68.   [2] ll. 2501–8.   [3] ll. 2910–21.

Let us return for a moment to the *Liber Historiae Francorum*. It was written two hundred years after the event, and its account is based on that of Gregory of Tours, even to the same phraseology. Yet it adds an important particular, the part played by the Hetware, not mentioned in any of the manuscripts of Gregory's work. It is possible that the author of this anonymous work was using a manuscript of Gregory's work to which additions had been made; but we must also envisage the possibility that, since he was in all probability a Neustrian Frank, that is to say, an inhabitant of the part of the Frankish territory in which Theuderic, and after him Theudebert, had reigned, he may have been in a position to draw on local traditions of events in this territory, and to supplement Gregory's account from some oral source. Both these Frankish kings were the heroes of popular song, and, although the stories relating to them which survive in the Middle High German poem of Hug-Dietrich and Wolf-Dietrich have become far removed from any historical basis, these later romantic tales must have been preceded by poems more closely related to the events of fifth-century history. It is possible that the defeat of Hygelac may have been one of the subjects of the songs about Theuderic which are mentioned by the anonymous Saxon poet who wrote *De gestis Caroli Magni* towards the end of the ninth century,[1] and that the author of the *Liber Historiae Francorum* drew his additional piece of information from such a source. It cannot be proved that he did, but the

[1] See Chambers, *Widsith*, p. 112.

mere possibility that the story of Hygelac's raid was still being related in the north-east of the Frankish realm in the eighth century prevents us from stating dogmatically that the English of this period knew the story solely from the Scandinavian point of view. Dr. Levison has made us acutely aware of the amount of cross-Channel intercourse in the seventh and eighth centuries,[1] and the English were interested enough in Theuderic (*Theodric*) for him to be mentioned in *Widsith*,[2] which poem also tells us the name of a king of the Hetware.[3] They very probably learnt of these persons by the direct route across the Channel, for it seems unnecessary to assume that, while the English in their continental home-land were hospitable to the legends of all tribes, as soon as they reached Britain they looked askance at any story which had not come from across the North Sea.

It is now time to turn to what used to be regarded as the third Frankish source for the history of Hygelac. In the *Liber Monstrorum* or *De Monstris et de Belluis*, 'concerning Monsters and Strange Beasts', there is a well-known passage: 'And there are monsters of a wonderful size; such as King Higlacus who ruled the *Getæ* and was killed by the Franks, whom from his twelfth year no horse could carry. His bones are preserved on an island in the Rhine, where it flows forth into the ocean, and are shown to those who come from afar as a miracle.'[4] This fills out the Hygelac tradition with detail not con-

---

[1] *England and the Continent in the Eighth Century* (Oxford, 1946).
[2] *Widsith*, l. 24.   [3] Hún, ibid., l. 33.
[4] M. Haupt, *Opuscula*, ii (Leipzig, 1876), 223.

tained in other sources, it supports the statement of the
Beowulf poet that his body remained in the enemies'
keeping, it calls him a king, not of the Danes, but of a
tribe with a name very like that of the Geats, and it
shows that people near the mouth of the Rhine remembered something of this king.

In 1924 M. Antoine Thomas wrote an article on a
newly discovered third manuscript of this Latin work,
in which he suggests that the work is not of Frankish
origin, but was written in England.[1] His view was
accepted by Lawrence, who refers to it briefly in 1928,[2]
and, by implication, by Chambers in the addenda to
the second edition of his *Beowulf: An Introduction*, in
1932;[3] but neither of these authorities goes into the
matter in detail, or examines the implications of this
theory for *Beowulf* studies. Yet it is obvious that if we
can accept this localization of the *Liber Monstrorum*, it
puts a very different complexion on the Hygelac
question.

M. Thomas makes a convincing case for his claim
that the newly found manuscript of this work, now at
Leyden, was copied from a manuscript written in
England. The text has some false readings occasioned
by the scribe's unfamiliarity with an abbreviation for
autem used only in the Insular script. This abbreviation
is very like the suspension of *hoc* or *haec* and thus the
copyist renders it. But still more significant is the spelling

---

[1] 'Un manuscrit inutilisé du Liber Monstrorum', *Archivum Latinitatis
medii aevi* (Bulletin Du Cange; Paris, 1925), pp. 232–45.
[2] *Beowulf and Epic Tradition*, p. 94.   [3] p. 504.

of the king's name as *Higlacus* in the text, *Hyglaco* in the rubric, for these are English forms of the name, and it would be very difficult to account for their presence in a continental manuscript except on the assumption that the scribe found them in his exemplar, and that that exemplar was written by an Englishman. It should also be noted that the other, later manuscripts of the work have the name in spellings closer to the English than the Frankish form of it. Thomas dates the Leyden manuscript for palaeographical reasons about the turn of the ninth and tenth centuries, too early, therefore, to allow of our attributing its presence at the abbey of St. Benedict of Fleury, to which it once belonged, to the close intercourse of that house with England in the mid-tenth century; but there is more than sufficient evidence of relations between English and continental religious houses during the eighth and ninth centuries for the passage of a work from England to France to occasion no surprise.

It is difficult to date precisely the work itself. Manitius[1] has shown that it uses St. Augustine's 'City of God', the 'Etymologies' of Isidore of Seville, the 'Chronicle', reaching to 534, of Marcellinus Comes, the rather rare work the *Historiarum Alexandri Magni Macedonis Libri X* of Quintus Curtius, and the *Physiologus*, so that it can hardly date from a time before Anglo-Latin scholarship was well advanced. The author's chief debt is to Virgil, and though he also refers to Lucan, it is thought possible

---

[1] See M. Manitius, *Geschichte der lateinischen Literatur des Mittelalters*, i (1911), 114–18.

that his knowledge of this poet may have been drawn from scholia to Virgil. As long as the work was believed to be of Frankish origin, the date assigned to it depended on the superiority of its Latin to that of the Merovingian age, but this criterion becomes valueless if the work was produced in England. It is held to be prior to the studies of Alcuin and Hrabanus Maurus, but that does not necessitate our putting it, as Thomas does, as early as 700; for no other reason, I suspect, than that he accepts that as the date of *Beowulf*, and assumes that two works referring to Hygelac are likely to be approximately contemporary.

We must consider what difference the attribution of this text to England makes to views formerly current on *Beowulf*. In the first place it robs us of continental support for Hygelac's Geatish nationality. The position now is simply that English sources call him a Geat and Frankish sources make him a Dane. The poet's statement that the king's body passed into the possession of the enemy may be not so much supported by this Latin work as based on it, or at least on the same travellers' tale that reached its author. But, if we have lost on the one hand, the gain on the other is heavy. For, if the *Liber Monstrorum* is an English work, it shows that Hygelac was known to the English quite apart from what they could learn from *Beowulf*, and thus it greatly increases the likelihood that the poet could rely on his hearers' previous knowledge of the Geatish kings as on that of the Danish kings, and could leave it to them to supply more than he chose to tell them. Secondly, it is of interest that familiarity with Hygelac should be revealed in the work of a man of some classical education, for we can put this fact beside Alcuin's complaint that monks are interested in Ingeld, and use it to show that some men of education did not despise the heroic tales. Finally, if it is true that bones were being shown as Hygelac's on an island in the Rhine to strangers from afar, would not this present an occasion on which the natives of the district and the foreigners might compare their versions of his story? A returning Englishman might come home not only with an account of the gigantic bones he had seen, but with a story of Hygelac's raid influenced by Frankish tradition. It should be borne in mind that during the latter years of the seventh century, and through most of the eighth, English missionaries had brought Frisia into very close relation with their own land, and hence it is not at all surprising that an English ecclesiastic should know what could be seen on an island in the Rhine.

There is something else about the *Liber Monstrorum* that perhaps has a bearing on *Beowulf* studies, though I am not at all sure what bearing. Hygelac is the only Germanic hero to be mentioned in it, and he is a monster solely on account of his great size. The reference to him precedes the frame of the main treatment, which concerns itself with the monsters of classical tales and the queer monstrosities which men were ready to believe to occupy remote lands, and which are derived, ultimately, from Greek sources. The author refers explicitly to one well-known source of such accounts,

namely, the letter supposed to have been written from
India by Alexander to Aristotle. He also draws pro-
lifically from another work of this kind, without men-
tioning it by name, a work generally known as the
'Marvels (or Wonders) of the East'.[1] Latin texts of both
these works occur in pre-Conquest manuscripts in
England.[2] What seems a very odd coincidence, if it is
nothing more, is that there should be this Latin work
using the 'Letter of Alexander to Aristotle' and the
'Marvels of the East', and referring to a character who
appears in *Beowulf*, when in our only surviving manuscript of *Beowulf* the poem is immediately preceded by
Old English versions of the 'Letter of Alexander to
Aristotle' and the 'Marvels of the East', written in the
same hand as the first part of *Beowulf*. But, if this is more
than coincidence, to what does it point? Could it be
that the *Beowulf* manuscript, or a predecessor that contained the same series of texts, was compiled at the same
centre which produced the *Liber Monstrorum*? If, however, there once was an earlier manuscript than that
which survives, with this combination of texts, it cannot
have been much earlier, for Dr. Sisam kindly allows me
to say that his researches have brought him to the
conclusion that the whole *Beowulf* codex collection was
assembled in the latter half of the tenth century, and
that the evidence is against any two of the pieces having
been put together much before 950.

[1] On this see M. R. James, *The Marvels of the East* (Roxburghe Club,
1929).

[2] The *Marvels* in Tiberius B. v, Alexander's Letter in Harleian MS.
2682.

The problem of the relation of the *Beowulf* manuscript to the *Liber Monstrorum* would be simpler if the reference to Hygelac in the latter work could have been derived solely from *Beowulf*, but that is obviously not the case. One could, however, visualize the author who collected his monsters from the classics, from Isidore, &c., from the 'Letter of Alexander' and the 'Marvels of the East' being reminded of Hygelac and his giant size because his library possessed a manuscript of *Beowulf*; and it would be possible that at some later date the Latin texts of the 'Letter' and the 'Marvels', which he used, were translated into English, and so were available, along with the poem, to be copied into our *Beowulf* manuscript. But I do not feel that this hypothesis carries much conviction. A simpler explanation could perhaps be offered. Persons interested in monsters might well be familiar with *Beowulf*, since it deals with supernatural creatures. It is doubtless this fact that brought the poem into its present company in the manuscript, as Dr. Sisam suggested,[1] and the compilation was presumably made by, or for, someone of similar interests to those of the author of the *Liber Monstrorum*. This author for his part may have called to mind a vernacular poem on monsters as he was compiling his material, and the poem may in its turn have reminded him of what he had heard tell of Hygelac's gigantic bones. It is true that he betrays no knowledge of the monsters of *Beowulf*, but then his main concern is with the monsters and marvels in Latin writers. Hygelac is

[1] K. Sisam, in *Rev. Eng. Stud.* x (1934), 342.

admitted only in the preliminary part of his work, as a marvel in which it is possible to believe. The mere fact that they were of popular, and not learned, origin, might be enough to disqualify Grendel and the dragon, and in any case the poet had given his dragon only the commonplace dragonesque characteristics, and had refrained from any precise description of Grendel's physical appearance. It would have been difficult to convey an impression of him in a few Latin sentences, and both he and the dragon might have looked tame beside some of the other monsters the author describes. The author could not point to Grendel's bones to prove that he was greater than any other man, as he could to Hygelac's. His failure to mention the Beowulfian monsters will not prove, therefore, that he did not know the poem, but nevertheless there is nothing in the passage on Hygelac to show that he did know it. It remains a possibility that monster-killing had not been connected with the royal family of the Geats in the version of the Hygelac story known to this writer. But I had meant to pose these problems rather than attempt to offer solutions, and merely to suggest that the *Liber Monstrorum* and the texts related to it might repay closer study. It is not without interest for its own sake, not least in its mention of a picture 'of Greek work', portraying an adventure of Ulysses.[1]

Although, as suggested above, there is a possibility that the story told in *Beowulf* of Hygelac's raid may have been influenced by Frankish tradition, it is not to be

[1] Haupt, op. cit., p. 245.

supposed that the poet knew it solely from that source;
he speaks of other events in Hygelac's life which took
place in Sweden and which would be most unlikely to
be known to the Franks, who believed Hygelac to be a
Dane. His sympathies seem to be on the Geatish side,
though perhaps that is only to be expected, when his
hero, the monster-killer Beowulf, is a Geat. Hygelac's
other exploits, together with the information about the
other kings of the Geats, cannot be corroborated from
outside evidence; for if, as Professor Malone suggests,
Hygelac is to be identified with the Hugleikr of the
Ynglingasaga and the Huglecus of Saxo,[1] and Hrethel
with Saxo's Roller,[2] the stories have become so altered
and garbled as to be worthless for comparison with
those of *Beowulf*. Yet, though corroboration for the kings
of the Geats is lacking, it is unlikely that the information
about them was the poet's invention. Most of their
adversaries, the kings of the Swedes, were remembered
in Scandinavian tradition, as well as some of the details
of the conflicts.[3] The poet's account of these matters is
scattered, and out of chronological order, so that modern
readers find it difficult to gather the sequence of events
without the aid of pencil and paper. We should,
perhaps, attribute to a contemporary audience, which
was denied such aids, a better memory than ours; even
so, the poet's method of recounting the wars between
the Geats and the Swedes hardly seems the natural way

[1] K. Malone, 'Hygelac', *Eng. Studies*, xxi (1939), 108–19.
[2] Id., 'Grendel and Grep', *Pub. Mod. Lang. Assoc. Amer.* lvii (1942),
1–14.
[3] See, e.g., Girvan, op. cit., pp. 70 f.

to instruct an ignorant audience; he never attempts to explain, for example, how Wiglaf's father, Weohstan, came to be fighting on the Swedish side.[1] A poet who was free to invent would presumably not have inserted puzzling features of this kind. The method of sketching in Geatish history certainly differs from the one used to depict the Danish background in the first part of the poem, where the audience had often to be content with a mere hint; but the greater fullness with which the Geatish wars are treated is capable of more than one explanation. It may be that the poet was less confident that his audience could supply all the relevant detail. No rulers of the Geats are mentioned in *Widsith* and it is possible that their stories were not so universally known. Professor Girvan has reached, in agreement with Olrik, the conclusion that the two series of events, Danish and Geatish, have each a different type of source behind them, namely, 'that the poet knew Geat history, but only Danish heroic tradition as preserved in poetry'.[2] The poet might have been more interested in accounts of international battles, or have expected his audience to have been particularly interested in them; or, finally, he might have found the dragon story so much thinner than the tale of the haunted hall, that he had to make fuller use of any material at his disposal.

In addition to these two main series of events, many other stories are referred to, and it is obvious that these

[1] ll. 2612–25. Weohstan was remembered in Scandinavian tradition as Vésteinn, but his affinities with both Swedes and Geats are not accounted for.

[2] Op. cit., p. 71.

passages will have greater force and colour to persons who know the story behind the allusion. It would be tedious to go through them all to demonstrate a fact so generally acknowledged, but some have a more particular interest. Sometimes the stories to which the poet is referring are recoverable, though not necessarily in just the form in which the poet and his contemporaries knew them. One of the more obscure allusions is to Hama, who, fleeing from Eormenric, 'bore to the bright city the necklace of the Brosings' and 'chose eternal gain (*ecne ræd*)'.[1] It is unlikely that this last phrase means only that he died, for Hrothgar advises Beowulf later on to choose *ece rædas*. If it were permissible to use the evidence of the thirteenth-century *Þiðrekssaga* to elucidate this passage,[2] one might see in these words a reference to Hama's entering a monastery, and if we could be sure that the poet meant that Hama bore his necklace into the keeping of the Church, the contrast with Hygelac, who is mentioned immediately afterwards, would be striking; for he wore his when he went raiding a peaceful people, and thus lost it to his enemies. But such reasoning would be oversubtle and insecure. It may be safer to follow Klaeber in seeing in *Beowulf* only the initial stage of the Christianization of the legend,[3] and in taking the phrase under consideration to mean that he became a Christian, the monastery being a later development. If it does mean this, it seems to me likely

---

[1] ll. 1198–1201.
[2] Chap. 288, 429. See, e.g., Chambers, *Widsith*, pp. 54–7.
[3] Klaeber, p. 179.

that the tale of a *wreccea* who turned to Christianity
would not have become so wide-spread that the poet
can mention it thus casually, until the English had been
Christian for a considerable time. Yet, since it cannot be
shown what, if anything, was the connexion between
the necklace of the Brosings and the *Brísinga men* of Old
Norse sources, it is probably unwise to build anything
at all on a reference so little understood.

On the other hand, it is not safe to argue from the
poet's silence that certain features of a story as recorded
in later records were unknown in his day. The poet is
sometimes assumed to be ignorant of the form of the
Sigemund tale in which Fitela was Sigemund's son by
his incestuous union with his sister;[1] or, alternatively,
to have suppressed this fact out of consideration for the
susceptibilities of his audience; yet it is possible that
both he and it were fully aware of this feature, and
that the poet's 'uncle to his nephew'[2] is a deliberate
use of understatement—*nepos, vel plus quam nepos*, a
later age might have expressed it—employed for ironic
effect.

And sometimes the stories are not recoverable. It is
on these occasions only fair to our poet to suppose that
when we see no point, or little point, in an allusion, the
fault lies in our lack of evidence, seeing that when we
know the story in question we can distinguish an
artistic purpose in his introduction of it. There is, however, one episode which has seemed to generations of
scholars so violently introduced and so lacking in artistic

---

[1] As related in *Vǫlsungasaga*, chap. 7.   [2] l. 881.

justification, that they have suspected that its presence is to be ascribed to other than artistic reasons. This is the Offa episode,[1] and it is of particular importance, because the suggestion is that it was introduced, either by the poet or an interpolator, in a determination to get in a reference to this Anglian hero. If one believes that the poet himself added the episode for this reason, then he was presumably an Anglian, or at least composing his poem for an Anglian patron.

As things stand, the introduction of the episode is violent indeed, and much ingenuity has been exercised in attempts to interpret a text which is certainly corrupt. The story of a queen who was arrogant and cruel until her marriage with King Offa seems to be brought in for no better reason than that Hygelac's young wife, Hygd, was not like her; Hygd was not niggardly, and immediately we hear about Offa's queen, though we are not told that she was niggardly either, so that the connexion is by no means obvious. But there is a new factor to be considered, a note by Dr. Sisam, who suggests that the first half-line of the episode, *modþryðo wæg*, usually supposed to contain the name of the lady, either as *Þryð* or *Modþryð*, is in reality parallel to lines like *hygeþryðe wæg*, *modsorge wæg*, &c., recorded elsewhere.[2] It would therefore mean only something like 'she was proud'. He suggests that there is a lacuna in the text before this half-line, caused by the scribe's eye having dropped to

[1] ll. 1931–62.
[2] K. Sisam, 'Notes on Old English Poetry', *Rev. Eng. Stud.* xxii (1946), 266 n.

another line with the same alliteration as the one he was copying. Dr. Sisam's argument seems to me convincing, and, if a few lines have been lost, we can hardly wonder that the transition sounds abrupt. The missing lines may have made clear the connexion between the story of Offa's queen, now nameless, and Hygd.

The story cannot be found elsewhere in a close enough form to throw light on the matter, although the late twelfth-century St. Albans work, the *Vitae duorum Offarum*, gives an account of the wife of King Offa of Mercia which has no relation at all to that historical lady and is agreed to have been transferred to her from the wife of the earlier Offa, king of Angel.[1] This personage is described as a wicked character, and is called Drida, i.e. *Þryð*. This at first sight would seem to disprove Dr. Sisam's contention that the half-line discussed above did not contain this name; but only at first sight, for the postulated error of jumping a few lines would be still easier to understand if both half-lines—the one the scribe should have copied and the one his eye caught by mistake—contained the word *þryð*, in the one case as a proper name, in the other as an element of a compound. But the story of Drida has moved too far away from that known to the *Beowulf* poet to help us to decide whether this allusion had any relevance to the character of Hygd.

If, however, in justice to the poet, one must admit the possibility that to contemporaries there may have been an obvious sequence of thought that led from Hygd to

[1] *Vitae duorum Offarum*, relevant sections ed. Chambers, pp. 217–43.

Thryth, and so acquit him, for want of evidence, from the charge of dragging in the whole story, I nevertheless am left with the impression that, when he had once launched on the story of Thryth, he left her very rapidly in order to sing the praises of Offa, as if that had been his real purpose in introducing this digression. Offa is 'the prince of warriors, the best of all mankind, of the human race, between the seas; for Offa, a man bold in war, was widely renowned for his bounty and his battles, and maintained his country by wisdom'. The poet speaks with praise of other kings, but surely never quite in these superlative terms.

It is reasonable to suppose that the audience which listened to this eulogy knew something of the deeds of Offa, apart from his dealings with his wife; that it was acquainted with the story alluded to in *Widsith* and related fully in much later sources both in England and Denmark, a story telling how he defended his country in successful single combat against two enemy champions. The details need not concern us. The surviving English version, the St. Albans work already mentioned, locates the whole affair in England; the Danish sources, the chronicle of Sweyn Aageson, the *Annales Ryenses*, and the *Historia Danica* of Saxo Grammaticus,[1] place it on an island in the River Eider; but this discrepancy is probably to be attributed to a late

---

[1] *Svenonis Aggonis filii Compendiosa Regum Daniae Historia a Skioldo ad Canutum VI*, ed. J. Langebek, *Scriptores Rerum Danicarum*, i. 44–7; *Annales Ryenses*, ed. id., p. 152; *Saxonis Gesta Danorum*, ed. J. Olrik and H. Ræder, i. 92–100. The first and the last authorities are printed by Chambers, pp. 206–15, the second by Klaeber, p. 262.

alteration in the English form of the story, and the two versions are otherwise in major agreement. It is usual to take the facts on which they agree to be features of the original legend, faithfully and independently preserved on both sides of the North Sea. But ought one not to take into consideration the very close contact between England and Denmark right from the time of Cnut the Great until the date when these works were being written? There is evidence for strong English influence on the Danish Church and the Danish court, on Danish coinage, Danish seals, Danish art-motifs; it seems dangerous to assume that there could be no interchange of ideas in the province of story-telling. The Offa story in England was preserved at St. Albans Abbey, a foundation of Offa the Great, and the connexions of this place with Denmark are particularly well-evidenced. About 1085 King Cnut Sveinsson presented a shrine with relics of St. Alban to the church of Odense, and it has been suggested that they were brought over by the Canterbury-born monk Æthelnoth, who seems to have come to Denmark about this time and who, after the king had been murdered in this very church, wrote his biography.[1] The later St. Albans historians had a much garbled story of the taking of the relics of their saint to Denmark by the Danish raiders of England in the days of an early tenth-century abbot, and, though little credence is to be given to this tale, the authorities quoted for it are of interest in

---

[1] *Ælnothi Monachi Historia ortus, vitæ, et passionis S. Canuti Regis Daniæ*, ed. Langebek, op. cit., iii. 325–90.

demonstrating the intercourse between St. Albans and
Denmark; for they are given as 'reliable, discreet and
trustworthy men, born or brought up in the district of
St. Albans, who lived for many years in Denmark in
the service of the Lord King of Denmark'.[1] The king
in question is Waldemar the Great (1157–82), father
of the King Waldemar to whom Saxo dedicated his
'History of the Danes', and the men referred to are Odo,
this king's treasurer and banker, Master John of St.
Albans, an incomparable goldsmith, his son Nicholas of
St. Albans, who was Waldemar's mintmaster for thirty
years, and afterwards mintmaster to the King of
England, the cleric Edward, counsellor of the English
king, and his nephew. We also read of an Anketil, a
monk of St. Albans, at one time moneyer to the Danish
king, who returned to England and made a shrine for
St. Alban in 1129.[2] Without going the whole way with
Müllenhoff, who considered the Offa story an importa-
tion from England into Denmark,[3] one can see that
there was plenty of opportunity for English and Danish
stories to influence one another.[4]

---

[1] *Gesta Abbatum Monasterii Sancti Albani*, ed. H. T. Riley, *R.S.* 1867,
i. 13–19; H. G. Leach, *Angevin Britain and Scandinavia* (Harvard Studies
in Comparative Literature, vi, 1921), p. 28; L. F. R. Williams, *History
of the Abbey of St. Alban* (London, 1917), pp. 23 f.

[2] *Gesta Abbatum Monasterii Sancti Albani*, i. 83–4; Williams, op. cit., pp. 61 f.

[3] K. Müllenhoff, *Beovulf: Untersuchungen über das angelsächsische Epos
und die älteste Geschichte der germanischen Seevölker* (1889), pp. 72–84. He was
opposed by A. Olrik, 'Er Uffesagnet invandret fra England? Bemærk-
ninger til Müllenhoff's "Beovulf" ', *Ark. f. nord. Filologi*, viii (N. F. iv),
368–75. The Offa legend has produced a large critical literature, for
which see the bibliographies in the works of Chambers, Klaeber, &c.

[4] It is a pity we do not know more about Lucas, a man from Britain,

But with *Widsith* we are on firmer ground. It too speaks in the highest terms of Offa:

Offa ruled Angel, Alewih the Danes. He was the bravest of all these men; yet he did not out-do Offa in deeds of valour, but Offa was the first of men who won for himself while still a youth the greatest of kingdoms. No-one of his age did in battle greater deeds of valour with a single sword. He marked out a boundary against the Myrgings, by *Fifeldore* (the River Eider). The English and the Swæfe have held it ever since as Offa won it.[1]

Just as the *Beowulf* poet reserved his superlative praise for Offa, so the *Widsith* poet goes to more trouble to sing his praises than those of any other king; yet, from what can be gathered about his story, he does not seem so outstanding above all the ranks of heroes. Is it then tribal patriotism that makes the poets speak of him thus? If so, the poems must be Anglian, probably Mercian, for it was only this royal house that included Offa in its genealogy. Could we go further and surmise that the poets praise extravagantly a king called Offa in compliment to a descendant and namesake? It is tempting to take the definite reference to a boundary in *Widsith* as a complimentary reminder that a greater Offa built a greater boundary, Offa's Dyke. I can accept this more easily than Sir Cyril Fox's suggestion that Offa the Great modelled his career on that of his distant ancestor.[2]

who was secretary to Prince Christopher and in 1170 incited the fainting Danish forces to fight to avenge their fallen comrades by relating history to them. *Saxonis Gesta Danorum* (ed. J. Olrik and H. Ræder, i. 479) says he was slightly educated in letters, but especially learned in knowledge of history. See Leach, op. cit., p. 141.   [1] *Widsith*, ll. 35–44.
[2] 'The Boundary Line of Cymru', *Proc. Brit. Acad.* xxvi (1940), 292 f.

It is many years since Earle suggested that *Beowulf* was
composed at Offa's court;[1] he supported his view by
several arguments and assumptions which are untenable,
and it has usually been rejected as impossible on linguistic grounds. I do not think that a date 757–96 can
be proved impossibly late for either *Beowulf* or the Offa
section of *Widsith*, and so I would regard it a possible
hypothesis that our poem originated at the court of
Offa the Great, a possible and an attractive hypothesis, but one incapable of proof.

It is now time to turn to the main theme of the poem,
to see if there is any sign that the audience knew that
story to start with. Can we decide whether the poet
expected it to derive pleasure from a familiar tale well
told, or whether it was now to be treated to a new
story put into a familiar setting? I am not alone in
believing that enough evidence is forthcoming to show
that the *Beowulf* poet was not the first to make the hall
of the Scyldings the scene of a monster's visitations. In
spite of very great differences—natural enough when
it is remembered that some six centuries separate the
two works—there are enough points of contact between
the *Beowulf* account of the cleansing of Heorot and that
in the Saga of Hrolf Kraki[2] of the liberation of this
king's hall from a monster's ravages to suggest that the
deliverance of the Danish royal hall was a story known
before the *Beowulf* poet took up the theme. It is un-

[1] J. Earle, *The Deeds of Beowulf* (Oxford, 1892), pp. lxxv–c.
[2] *Hrólfs Saga Kraka*, chap. 23, ed. Finnur Jónsson, pp. 65–71; relevant
portions, with English translation, Chambers, pp. 138–46; translation
by S. M. Mills, pp. 52–8.

necessary to elaborate a matter which has frequently
been exhaustively dealt with.[1] The fact that in both
versions the deliverer comes from the land of the Geats
and is also concerned in the slaying of Onela (Áli) and
the placing of Eadgils (Aðils) on his throne is enough
to establish an original identity, quite apart from minor
similarities.

Yet the type of haunting of the Danish hall in these
two versions is very dissimilar. The assailant in the saga
is a winged beast, who makes annual visitations at
Yuletide. We are told nothing of its haunts, and there
appears no avenging mother, who has to be traced to her
lair. There is no evidence to let us decide whether it was
the Scandinavian or the English version which departed from the original form of the story. One might
hazard the guess that the original deliverer was already
known, like Beowulf, as a dragon-killer also, and that
in the saga his two feats have been telescoped into one,
with the result that a dragon-like beast has replaced an
anthropomorphic monster at the Danish court; but it
would only be a guess, incapable of substantiation. It is
open for us to believe, if we wish, that the *Beowulf* poet
was original in choosing to place this particular tale of
haunting in the hall of the Scyldings. Not that the tale
itself was new; the analogues to it elsewhere, especially
that in the *Grettissaga*,[2] prove too clearly that a tale of
ravaging by water-monsters, very similar to that of

[1] e.g. Chambers, pp. 54–61; Berendsohn, op. cit., 211–28.
[2] *Grettis Saga Ásmundarsonar*, chaps. 32–5, 64–6, ed. Guðni Jónsson,
(Reykjavík, 1936), pp. 107–23, 209–17; relevant portions, with translation, Chambers, pp. 146–82.

Grendel and his mother, existed apart from this setting, and there is nothing to show us whether the poet took it over already located at Heorot, or whether he replaced with it a different tale of a monster's attacks.

As for the audience, did it know this story, either in this setting or outside it? There is a faint hint that the hero may have been known apart from the poem. It may not mean much that actual persons occasionally bore his name, i.e. a Biuulf in the *Liber Vitae* of Lindisfarne,[1] and a Bowulf in Devon in a Pipe-Roll of 1195,[2] but if, as the editors of *The Place-Names of Devon* suggest, the form *bigulfesburh* in a thirteenth-century copy of a charter of 1061 is to be interpreted 'Beowulf's *burh*',[3] this may be the hero, for the place referred to, Belbury Castle, is an ancient camp, and to such structures the names of legendary figures were sometimes applied. The name Grendel crops up in place-names, as in *grendlesmere* in a Wiltshire charter of 931, and in other places of this name in Essex and in Worcestershire, *Grendelesbiry* and *grendelespytt* in Devon, and *grendeles gata* in Middlesex; but it is not certain that it is not a common noun, for a water-course.[4] The poet introduces his villain as a *mære mearcstapa* 'a famous (or notorious) haunter of the borderlands';[5] but does this mean

[1] H. Sweet, *The Oldest English Texts* (E.E.T.S., 1885), p. 163; facsimile in *Publications of the Surtees Society*, cxxxvi (1923), fol. 34 v.

[2] *The Place-Names of Devon* (English Place-Name Society, IX), ii. 604.

[3] Ibid., pp. 603 f.

[4] See, e.g., Chambers, pp. 44, 304–10, 506; R. E. Zachrisson, 'Grendel in Beowulf and in Local Names', *A Grammatical Miscellany offered to Otto Jespersen* (Copenhagen and London, 1930), pp. 39–44.

[5] l. 103.

notorious to his audience, or merely to the Danes of his story?

On the whole, if we want to know if this was a familiar tale to the audience, we are again thrown back to a consideration of the poet's method of telling his tale, to see if he leaves parts incomplete or vague because his audience can fill in the gaps. Personally, I think that most of the difficulties in relation to the main theme of the poem are the creation of scholars, who look in the poem for certain features that are clear in this or that analogue, and then blame the poet for obscuring them if they fail to discover them. There is no distinct picture of a cave behind a waterfall, as in the *Grettissaga*; but is it certain that the poet meant to describe one? He describes a hall at the bottom of a lake. Writers on *Beowulf* may refer to a cave as the scene of Beowulf's second encounter, but the poet never does. He calls it a *hof*, a *niðsele*, a *hrofsele*, a *reced*, a *hus*, all terms that apply to a building, rather than a natural cave. It is free from water, because it is a roofed-hall;[1] the poet clearly implies that the roof keeps out the water, and we need not worry about the laws of gravity, in a haunted mere so reminiscent of the lake of hell in the 'Vision of St. Paul'.[2] If, as seems probable, a waterfall was a feature of the original story, the vagueness of the

[1] ll. 1514–16.

[2] R. Morris, *The Blickling Homilies* (E.E.T.S., 1880), pp. vi f., was the first to notice the similarity between *Beowulf*, lines 1357–64, 1414–17, and a passage clearly drawn from some version of the *Visio S. Pauli* at the end of the seventeenth Blickling Homily, pp. 209 f. Agreement has not been reached whether the poet knew the *Visio*, or the homilist the poem.

poet's description is to be attributed less to a knowledge
that his hearers can themselves supply precise details,
than to a transference of the action to a different type
of scenery.

It has been suggested that the poet has not made his
meaning clear in another place. The hero is in a desper-
ate position, stretched on the floor with the ogress on
top of him; he is weaponless, for his sword has failed him,
and only his corselet saves him from instant destruction.
But 'the wise Lord, the Ruler of the Heavens, easily
decided it rightly when he stood up again'.[1] Now in
some analogues, divine intervention took the form of a
miraculous ray, and the suggestion is that so it did here,
only the poet forgot to tell us so—or at least did not
trouble to do so. But perhaps it did not, and perhaps
the poet thought he had said all that was necessary
when he said that the hero caught sight of a giant
sword. Was not that a sight to give heart to a weaponless man? The hero regarded it as providential; he says
later: 'But the Ruler of men permitted me to see hanging on the wall a beautiful, mighty sword—very often
has He guided the friendless man.'[2] I can see no need
for a miraculous light. Neither can I follow Chambers
and others and see a discrepancy in the poet's account
of how Beowulf reached the she-monster's lair. She
grabbed him in the water and bore him into her *hof*,
where a fire was burning; he could not use his weapons
against her in the water, because he was harassed by
water-beasts. But when in her court, free from these

[1] ll. 1554–6.   [2] ll. 1661–4.

assailants, by the light of the fire 'the goodly man perceived a she-wolf of the depths, a mighty sea-woman'.[1] It is natural enough that this was the first moment when he was able to perceive just what it was that had got hold of him in the water; yet it has been argued from this passage that 'the original version was one which represented the hero as free: penetrating the cave, seeing the monster, and attacking her'.[2] The poet is surely too good an artist to have failed to make up his mind which form of a story he is going to tell, and an audience skilled and alert enough to follow his allusive style would hardly have been content with clumsy contradictions in his main narrative.

As for the dragon episode, there are no very precise parallels for comparison. The closest is the story in Saxo of how the Danish king Frotho killed a dragon,[3] and, though it may be true, as Chambers is at pains to demonstrate,[4] that the points of similarity are commonplace features of dragon-fights, the mere fact that Scandinavian tradition attributed a dragon-killing to the Danish king who occupies in the genealogies precisely the place of Beowulf the Dane, son of Scyld, in the poem of *Beowulf*, is something which Beowulfian scholars cannot ignore. The suggestion that Beowulf the Geat became regarded as a dragon-slayer by confusion with his namesake Beowulf the Dane is no

[1] ll. 1518 f.
[2] Chambers, p. 470, referring to Müllenhoff's opinion in *Zeit. f. deut. Altertum*, xiv (1869), 210.
[3] *Saxonis Gesta Danorum*, ed. J. Olrik and H. Ræder, i. 36–7.
[4] Chambers, pp. 93–7.

more far-fetched than many theories that have won
general recognition. The confusion of namesakes is a
common enough phenomenon in stories handed down
by oral tradition; one may compare the confusion of
Siward *Digri* 'the Stout' of Northumbria with the
Orkney earl.[1] Such a theory implies, of course, that the
alteration of the name of Scyld's son, from the Beaw
(Beo) of the genealogies to Beowulf, had already taken
place in whatever source the poet had for his knowledge of the kings of the Danes. Those who prefer to
regard Beowulf the Dane as the outcome of scribal error
in the transmission of the poem must dismiss Frotho's
dragon-slaying as an irrelevant coincidence.

I would conclude this section by saying that one
cannot state with confidence that the audience knew
the main plot of the poem beforehand; but neither can
one state that it did not, for a poet might well be
expected to tell his main tale fully and clearly, however
vague he might be allowed to be about an illustrative
parallel.

[1] *Vita et Passio Waldevi*, ed. J. A. Giles, *Vita* [sic] *Quorundum* [sic]
Anglo-Saxonum (Caxton Society, 1854), pp. 5–9. See A. Olrik, 'Sivard den
digre', *Ark. f. nord. Filologi*, xix (Lund, 1903), 214.

III

IT is now time to assemble evidence which may help us to assess the audience's attitude to what the poet has to tell it. The attitude to the Christian religion and to the ethics of the blood-feud has already been dealt with, because of its bearing on the date, and we reached the conclusion that the audience was familiar with the teachings of the Church and accepted them without question, and that it acknowledged the obligations of the blood-feud. The next important issue is its attitude to the supernatural creatures with which the story deals.

I have deliberately avoided the terminology 'historical element' and 'fabulous element', speaking instead of 'main theme' and 'sub-theme' or 'illustrative matter', because I believe that the former distinction would have seemed artificial to a contemporary audience. In fact, if one could have quoted to one of them Lawrence's description of Anglo-Saxon epic as 'the addition of history to fairy-tale',[1] I think he would have been puzzled by it. He would have felt that at one stage of its history the hall Heorot was delivered from a monster's ravages, at another, it became the scene of an attack by Ingeld and the Heathobards; these events would not seem on different levels. After all, it was the one demonstrably historical character in the poem who was admitted into a 'Book of Monsters'. The average man

[1] W. W. Lawrence, *Medieval Story*, 2nd edit. (New York, 1926), p. 69.

would believe in the monsters, in the creatures of evil lurking in the waste lands round him. It is not necessary to give mythological or allegorical significance to the monsters before the central theme can achieve dignity. Though naturally it is easy for such creatures to take on a symbolical meaning, the account of the rescue of a people from the ravages of monsters would seem no less worthy of serious treatment than that of its delivery from a hostile army.

The work of the English Place-Name Society has in late years made it clear how deep-seated and wide-spread was the belief in goblins and ogres who haunted remote places. A common element in place-names is *puca* 'goblin', or its diminutive *pucel*. (This word does not happen to be used in *Beowulf*, but then, what poet would land himself in the difficulties of alliterating on *p* when there were so many other names at his disposal?) Fourteen place-names in Wiltshire, eighteen in Sussex, are known to have contained it, and several of them, as well as some in Devon, Northamptonshire, Cambridgeshire, &c., show it compounded with a second element meaning 'pit', 'pool', 'hole', 'brook', or 'well'. It is evident, therefore, that it frequently denotes a water-goblin.

Þyrs, a term applied to Grendel in the poem, also occurs in place-names, commonly compounded with similar elements, as in Tusmore, Oxfordshire, which means 'the mere of the *þyrs*', as does a lost name in the East Riding of Yorkshire. There is a *þyrs*-pit in Worcestershire, another in Warwickshire, two in Cambridgeshire, half a dozen in Northamptonshire. In Lancashire it is compounded with words meaning ravine or valley, three times in all, in Norfolk with 'ford'; in Derbyshire there is a cave, Thirst (or Thirse) House, and two caves in Staffordshire are similarly called after this super-natural creature;[1] *Thyrspittes*, *Thrusmyre*, *Thruswelker* 'ogre-spring-marsh', occur in medieval documents relating to Lincolnshire.[2]

Both the *scinna* and the *scucca* of *Beowulf* l. 939 have left their mark on place-nomenclature, the former on Skinburness in Cumberland (*scinnanburh*) and perhaps on Shinburgh, Essex, and Shincliffe, County Durham; the latter more commonly, compounded either with words for water-courses or pits, as in Shobrooke, Devon, Shocklach, Cheshire, and *Schokepit*, Cambridgeshire, or with words for hill, as in Shucknall, Herefordshire, or—more interestingly—for 'barrow', as in Shucklow Warren (*scuccanhlau*) in Buckinghamshire, Shuckburgh, Warwickshire, Shugborough, Staffordshire.[3] More often, and more to our purpose, names for tumuli indicate the belief that these were inhabited by dragons. 'Dragon's mounds' are commemorated at Drakelow in Derbyshire and another place of the same name in Worcestershire,

---

[1] See F. Haverfield, 'Romano-British Remains', in *Vict. C. Hist. of the County of Derby*, i (1905), 233 ff.—a reference which I owe to Sir Frank Stenton.

[2] B. Dickins, 'Yorkshire Hobs', *Trans. Yorks. Dialect Soc.*, vii (1942), 14. The whole of this interesting and amusing paper is important for study-ing the lingering of the belief in the *þyrs* and other monsters in post-Conquest times. For pre-Conquest evidence, see the same writer's 'English Names and Old English Heathenism', *Essays and Studies*, xix (1934), 156–60.   [3] Ibid., p. 157.

at Dragley in Lancashire, and at a lost *Draclowe* in Northamptonshire. Though the other Old English word for a dragon, *wyrm*, may mean merely 'snake' or 'worm' in most of its occurrences in place-names, there can be little doubt that in Wormwood Hill, Cambridgeshire (*wyrmelawe*), where there is a tumulus surviving, it must mean 'dragon', or rather 'dragons', for it is in the genitive plural. One should add to this list the Wiltshire *drakenhorde*, 'dragon's hoard', the Surrey *Drakehull*, the Lancashire *Drakeholm*, the Nottinghamshire Drakeholes, and the Warwickshire Drakenage. The belief in the dragon who inhabited mounds is expressed also in the Scandinavian names of the north of England, such as *Drechowe* in the North Riding of Yorkshire.[1]

Wiltshire, a much haunted county, affords—besides all its examples of *puca*, &c.—an instance of a Giant's Grave (with which one can compare the *entanhlew* in a charter of 940 relating to Polhampton, Hampshire), of a Giant's Cave, a *grendlesmere* and a *nikerpole*, and thus has most of the fauna of *Beowulf*. Other nickerpools existed in Lincoln[2] and in Sussex, and the same water-monster haunted a *Nikeresaker* in Cambridgeshire and a *Nikersmadwe* and a *Nickurlands* in Essex.[3]

This list does not claim to be exhaustive. The place-names of the various counties have been very unequally

[1] The Old Norse word for 'barrow' is also compounded with O.E. *scucca* and O.N. *skratti*, both meaning 'demon'.

[2] J. W. F. Hill, *Medieval Lincoln* (Cambridge, 1948), p. 363.

[3] The material for the preceding paragraphs has been drawn mainly from the English Place-Name Society's volumes, with use also of E. Ekwall, *The Place-Names of Lancashire* (Manchester, 1922), and *The Oxford Dictionary of English Place-Names*, 2nd edit. 1940.

studied; many of the instances come from minor names which are no longer in use and whose existence was unknown until the English Place-Name Society began to publish its material. Doubtless many other names of this type will come to light as more counties are systematically studied. In those counties already surveyed by the Society, this type of name is noticeably thickest in those of them, like Wiltshire and Sussex, for which a fair amount of early material is available. Minor names are easily replaced, and it is extremely probable that many names that once contained such elements have perished beyond recovery. This makes all the more impressive the amount of evidence that does survive.

Thus it will be seen that the evidence of place-names supports well the statements of the Cotton Gnomic Poem that 'a dragon, old, proud of its treasure, shall (be) in a mound' and 'a *þyrs* shall inhabit the fens, alone in the depths of the country'[1]—statements made in the same matter-of-fact tone as others like 'a wolf, the wretched lone-dweller, shall (be) in the wood' or 'stars shall shine bright in the heavens'.[2] Many charms survive from Anglo-Saxon times which afford evidence of belief in surrounding evil powers against which incantations and rituals are, or may be, effective. The mid-eighth-century Latin *Life of St. Guthlac*, written by Felix, perhaps shows better than all this how ready

[1] I owe to Professor Dickins the suggestion that this is the meaning of *innan lande* in this context.

[2] *Cotton Gnomic Poem*, ll. 18 f., 26 f., 42 f., 48 f.

were the men of this age, men quite likely to be our poet's contemporaries, to people the fens with monsters and demons; one should note in particular the remark that many men tried to inhabit an island there, but could not 'on account of the unknown monsters of the waste land and terrors of diverse shapes'.[1]

Perhaps the strongest evidence of all for belief in monsters is that it was found necessary to fit them into a Christian universe. If poet and audience had thought of Grendel and his kind as figments of the imagination, the poet would not have gone to such trouble to explain their descent. He was, of course, obliged to speak of Grendel's origin, once he had let Hrothgar's minstrel sing a song about the Creation, ending, with a reminiscence of the biblical 'and He created every living and moving creature', in the words:

> lif eac gesceop
> cynna gehwylcum þara þe cwice hwyrfað.

'He created life also for every species of those who move alive.'[2]

To introduce an ogre immediately on top of that, unexplained, would have left him as part of God's creation. So we are told of the evil progeny of Cain. Yet the poet does not introduce this as a mere explanatory comment, in passing; he explicitly reminds his audience of Grendel's descent from Cain in his recapitulation at the beginning of his second episode,[3] and he keeps alive the idea between these references

---

[1] *Vita Sancti Guthlaci*, ed. W. de G. Birch, *Memorials of St. Guthlac* (Wisbech, 1881), p. 17.

[2] ll. 97 f.   [3] ll. 1261–6.

with phrases like 'he bore God's anger'[1] or 'he, hostile
against God'.[2] And anyhow, the poet, if he had not
wished, was not forced to make the minstrel sing of the
Creation. It was his choice, not his necessity, and I
suggest that one reason for this choice was that this
theme led so well up to a discussion of the origin of
these creatures of evil. The poet wished to show that
they were not coeval with God; they did not exist
before the creation of the world; they were not part of
that creation; they were the offspring of sinful humanity,
the progeny of the first murderer. And they could be
successfully opposed by human beings who trusted in
God, as Beowulf did: 'He trusted for mercy, consolation
and help to the Almighty; for that reason he overcame
the enemy, brought low the hell-spirit.'[3]

It is in this context that I should like to face a difficulty in the general interpretation of the poem. The
characters put their trust in a Christian deity, and give
him thanks for their deliverance; moreover, we should
not perhaps be unduly worried that the poet lets them
be buried by ancient, spectacular burial rites, the
heathen implications of which may have become
blurred and forgotten. But early in the poem it is stated
that the Danes in their extremity had recourse to prayers
at heathen fanes, supplicating the devil for aid; and the
poem continues: 'Such was their custom, the hope of
heathens; they thought of hell in their hearts; they
knew not the Lord, the Judge of deeds, they knew not
the Lord God, nor could they praise the Protector of the

---

[1] l. 711.   [2] l. 811.   [3] ll. 1272–4.

Heavens, the Ruler of Glory' and so on with a tirade against the heathen.[1] It is therefore surprising to find that Hrothgar and Wealhtheow make constant appeals to the Christian God, whom, according to this passage, they did not know. I am inclined to think that the commonsense approach to this contradiction is to take this passage, at variance as it is with the whole spirit of the poem, as an interpolation,[2] particularly as it is not difficult to guess at a motive that might tempt a later poet to add it. It could be attributed to a man of the Viking Age, who could extract some comfort from the thought that, while the Danes were ravaging his country, they were bound straight for hell.

If, however, it seems an arbitrary and cowardly procedure to cut the knot like this, other explanations could be tried. The poet, who presumably knew that his characters really belonged to a pre-Christian age, may for once have departed from his usual practice of christianizing his material, while taking care to indicate that he had no sympathy with heathen practices. But I think it possible that he had a reason for the mention of this ineffective appeal to the wrong quarter. He may have been aware that some of his contemporaries attempted to safeguard themselves from molestation by malignant beings—such as the gods, elves, and witches mentioned in a well-known charm[3]—by

[1] ll. 175–88.   [2] As Professor Tolkien suggests, op. cit., p. 294, n. 34.
[3] H. Sweet, *An Anglo-Saxon Reader*, 11th edit., No. XIX B; E. van K. Dobbie, *The Anglo-Saxon Minor Poems* (The Anglo-Saxon Poetic Records VI), pp. 122 f.; G. Storms, *Anglo-Saxon Magic* (The Hague, 1948), pp. 140–51.

superstitious application to the powers of evil, instead of by invoking the aid of the Christian God, and may therefore have welcomed an opportunity of showing the futility of such a proceeding, by letting the Danes try it in vain. The passage would then be in line with clauses in ecclesiastical documents which are directed against the paying of honour to wells, or stones or other natural objects, a practice which may include the making of propitiatory offerings to the powers believed to inhabit such things. Precise references in English sources are from the post-Viking period,[1] but it should be noted that the synod of *Clofesho* of 747 thought it desirable to adopt in their statutes one from the Frankish capitulary communicated to them by St. Boniface, which impressed on bishops the need to suppress pagan observances in their dioceses.[2]

The poet did not invent his explanation of Grendel's origin. The idea of the giant brood of Cain is based on early interpretations of certain passages in Genesis,[3] and is frequently alluded to, occurring in the Old Saxon poem on Genesis,[4] among other places. The giants mentioned in Genesis were held to have perished in the Flood, as our poet states. One school of thought, therefore, derived later ogres and monsters from Noah's wicked son, Ham, but the *Beowulf* poet allows the

[1] e.g. Ælfric, *Catholic Homilies*, ed. B. Thorpe (1844), i. 474; id., *Lives of Saints*, ed. W. W. Skeat (E.E.T.S.), i. 372 f.; II Cnut 5. 1, together with the passages cited by A. J. Robertson in her note on this passage, *The Laws of the Kings of England*, p. 352.

[2] A. W. Haddan and W. Stubbs, *Councils and Ecclesiastical Documents*, (Oxford, 1871), iii. 364, 377 f.

[3] See p. 5 above.   [4] Old Saxon *Genesis*, ll. 807–12.

water-demons descended from Cain to survive the Flood. Emerson has shown that the belief that monsters were 'Cain's kin' is found in the Middle English poem, *Ywaine and Gawin*.[1]

It is of interest that Felix, the author of the Latin *Life of St. Guthlac*, should let the saint address his demon tormentors as 'the seed of Cain',[2] whereas the poem's based on this life make no such reference, and the still later Old English prose translation renders the expression *forwyrde tuddor* 'offspring of perdition'.[3] Thus in this mid-eighth-century work, which shares with our poem the conviction that marshes are the abodes of monsters, one gets support for the poet's view that evil broods are sprung from Cain. The points of contact between *Beowulf* and this Latin Life do not end there. There is, of course, a general similarity of theme, the poem telling how a deliverer saved human habitations from the ravaging of the monsters who haunted the 'misty moorlands' and the 'fen retreats', by physical struggle, and the Life describing how a hermit took up his abode on a haunted island in the fens and drove away the demons by spiritual conflict. Guthlac 'girded himself with spiritual weapons against the snares of the foul enemy; he turned into weapons for himself the shield of faith, the breastplate of hope, the helmet of chastity, the bow of patience, the arrows of psalmody';[4] a little farther on the arrows of the devil are mentioned. The

[1] Emerson, op. cit., p. 885.   [2] *Vita S. Guthlaci*, p. 28.
[3] P. Gonser, *Das angelsächsische Prosa-Leben des hl. Guthlac* (Anglistische Forschungen 27, 1909), p. 133.
[4] *Vita S. Guthlaci*, p. 19.

poet makes Hrothgar use the metaphor of spiritual armour against the devil's arrows in his warning speech to Beowulf on the dangers of pride.[1] The devil first came to attack Guthlac as he was singing psalms and canticles;[2] Grendel's hostility was aroused by the sound of festivity in Heorot, and the poet has given us as a sample of the entertainment a religious hymn sung by the minstrel.[3] Felix calls the devil *antiquus hostis prolis humanae*;[4] the poem uses similar terms of Grendel, e.g. *ealdgewinna, feond moncynnes*; but Felix's Latin terminology is not peculiar to him, and *feond moncynnes* occurs outside *Beowulf*, so these correspondences must not be pushed too far. Felix describes a rifled tumulus, above which Guthlac built his first hut, in words which would suggest a chamber-tomb if such were conceivable in this part of England;[5] the dragon in *Beowulf* guarded treasure in a chamber-tomb, which was rifled after its death.[6]

These resemblances are probably accidental; though it is not impossible that the poet was familiar with Felix's work and took some ideas from it. In any case they indicate a similarity of outlook, and they show that it is not only in works of the age of Bede that parallels to *Beowulf* can be found.

Felix's *Life of St. Guthlac* shows us that there were men who were not deterred from rifling a heathen barrow by the fear of a guardian dragon or of a curse on the

---

[1] ll. 1742–7. [2] *Vita S. Guthlaci*, p. 21. [3] ll. 86–101.
[4] *Vita S. Guthlaci*, p. 21. [5] Ibid., p. 20.
[6] ll. 2542–5, 2717–19, 2755–77, 3087–93, 3120–36.

treasure. Felix speaks with disapproval of their avarice. The *Beowulf* poet seems somewhat uncertain how the treasure in the dragon's mound should be regarded. It is heathen gold,[1] and there is a curse on it,[2] and yet he lets his hero die consoling himself that he has won so great a treasure for his people, and thanking God who has allowed him to do so.[3] His people do not benefit from his action, for it was decreed that the whole should be burned with Beowulf, presumably to do him honour;[4] but a Christian audience knows that gold, buried with the dead man, will do him no good in the after-life, and the poet permits himself a comment on the futility of this gesture: 'They let the earth hold the treasure of warriors, the gold in the ground, where it still lies, as useless to men as it was before.'[5] The Christian outlook has upset the older sense of values, surely. The trappings of the old tales on such themes have been kept, the pomp and ceremony of heathen burial rites, but neither poet nor audience can accept the implications of these rites.

As for these rites, the effect made by descriptions of them would certainly be different if the audience had actually seen such ceremonies, or heard them graphically described by an eyewitness, from what it would be if these things belonged to a date long before any of those who listened to the poem had been born. In the latter event, they might be familiar with such things only from traditional poetry—a description of a crema-

---

[1] l. 2276.   [2] ll. 3052, 3069–75.   [3] ll. 2794–801.
[4] ll. 3010–15.   [5] ll. 3166–8.

tion burial evidently formed a central scene in the Finn story,[1] for example—or from the accounts their grand-fathers had handed on. It has been argued that the detailed knowledge of these rites shown in the poem makes it desirable to date it as near to heathen days as is consistent with other evidence; or contrariwise, that the inexactitude of the accounts suggests a date at some distance from the time when these ceremonies were practised. It is for the archaeologist to adjudicate between these two views, but since the discoveries at Sutton Hoo have brought to light more material for comparison,[2] something must be said here on this question.

One result of this new find is that we need no longer charge the poet with inaccuracy on account of the rich-ness of the equipment in the burials he describes, nor even make allowance for poetic exaggeration. Also there are agreements between the furnishing of Scyld's ship-funeral and that supplied to the unknown person-age commemorated at Sutton Hoo; but these agree-ments are of a general nature, e.g. the presence in both funerals of treasures from distant lands, and the heap of treasures placed in the centre of the ship; for it cannot be considered established beyond doubt that a large and mysterious object at Sutton Hoo is equivalent to the *segen* which was placed high over Scyld's head.[3]

[1] Cf. ll. 1108–24.
[2] See, e.g., *The Sutton Hoo Ship-Burial: A Provisional Guide* (London: publ. by the Trustees of the British Museum, 1947); H. Maryon, 'The Sutton Hoo Helmet', *Antiquity*, xxi (1947), pp. 137–44.
[3] But see D. E. Martin-Clarke, in *The Early Cultures of North-West Europe* (H. M. Chadwick Memorial Studies, 1950), pp. 107–19.

Scyld's ship had a mast, whereas the Sutton Hoo ship was mastless, but this need not be a significant discrepancy, for one cannot argue from one ship without a mast that sailing ships were unknown at the date of the Sutton Hoo burial. The helmet found at this place has some affinities with those described in *Beowulf*,[1] but before this could be taken as a sign of an early date for the poem, it would be necessary to prove that the fashion in helmets changed, so that they were no longer made in this pattern in later times.

The funeral of Beowulf himself has been considered to possess irregular features, e.g. the hanging of helmets, shields, and corselets round the pyre, followed by the putting of unburnt rings and ornaments in the mound after the cremation.[2] If this could be put down to the poet's ignorance of what really happened at cremation funerals, and to his misunderstanding of the traditional accounts which had reached him, I should be well content; but in fair-mindedness one should remember that, if the procedure he describes is irregular, the circumstances are unusual also. A poet might feel that he could afford to do unorthodox, extravagant things with an enormous treasure which had just been won from a dragon; it is not safe to accuse him of ignorance of what was done at more normal funerals.

In any case, however, it is by no means certain that a description free from inaccuracy necessarily implies either first-hand experience or direct access to an eye-witness account. Perhaps one of the most important

[1] Especially ll. 303–6, 1448–54.   [2] ll. 3137–40, 3163–5.

contributions of the Sutton Hoo discovery to *Beowulf* studies is that it has made us change our ideas of the scale on which interments could take place in this country. Obsequies of this splendour were doubtless rare, but they must have been impressive and much talked of; men would describe them to their sons and grandsons; minstrels might sing of them and later poets imitate their phraseology. The finding of a ship-burial on this magnificent scale makes it easier to understand why men of a thoroughly Christian generation should still wish to hear of these ancient ceremonies. And it is sometimes forgotten how long a period can be covered by a couple of memories. Bede, who died in 735, has recorded a description of Paulinus, who left the North in 632, as it was given to Deda, abbot of Partney, by an old man who had seen Paulinus baptizing converts in the Trent.[1] That old man could have told Deda—and perhaps he did—many things about Anglo-Saxon heathenism. In some parts of England the heathen faith went on longer than it did in Northumbria, and the older members of an audience of about 750 were no farther removed from the days of Mercian heathenism than was Bede from Paulinus. An account need not develop glaring inaccuracies in a period of no longer than this, and I do not consider, therefore, that the burial customs in *Beowulf*, whether accurate or inaccurate, necessitate an early date for the poem.

We are not forced to believe that the poet's hearers knew of ship-burial or cremation from witnessing these

[1] *Historia Ecclesiastica* ii, chap. 16, ed. Plummer, op. cit., i. 117.

ceremonies. They would, however, have been familiar from experience with many other things described in the poem. Many of them may have felt the pull of conflicting emotions in the carrying out of a vendetta; only the very youngest among them would be without personal experience of warfare. If the audience were a Northumbrian one, he would have been a fortunate member of it who had never had to bear arms against his fellow-countrymen in support of someone's claim to the throne; and no matter when we date the poem, within the outside limits above mentioned, i.e. about 670–835, most members of the Northumbrian nobility would at some time have followed their king against foreign enemies, the Picts, the Britons, or the Mercians. Members of a Mercian audience would probably have played their part in the series of victorious campaigns which eventually made all the kingdoms of the South subject to their lord's overlordship; they may have fought in more defensive wars against Welsh raiders. Even during the period for which Bede's evidence is available, there was more warfare in England than he records; he was writing an ecclesiastical history and might ignore political events that had no bearing on this. We know of a Welsh attack on Mercia in the reign of Cenred (704–9) solely because it caused St. Guthlac to have unquiet dreams;[1] it must have been serious if news of it reached him far away in the east at Crowland, yet Bede does not refer to it. As for the period for which our evidence is much scantier, it is likely that

[1] *Vita S. Guthlaci*, pp. 29 f.

there was much warfare that is unrecorded. The *Life of St. Guthlac* shows that during the early years of the eighth century it was possible for a spirited young noble to collect a force and follow a career of warfare on his own account; and it is interesting to notice that what spurred Guthlac on to do so was that he remembered 'the strong deeds of ancient heroes'.[1] The West Saxons were frequently at war with the Mercians and with the Britons, the men of Kent tried to resist the power of Mercia; and in neither area was civil war unknown. We may take it that the poet of *Beowulf* spoke of battle to men who knew what these things meant.

Some of them may have had to support their lords in times of exile, hardship, and danger. One of the members of the court of Æthelbald of Mercia can be shown to have shared his exile before he came to the throne;[2] as an exile, this king had with him a band of followers when he came to visit Guthlac,[3] and this example of a comitatus sharing its leader's wanderings is by no means isolated. The poet's demand of absolute fidelity to a lord was no mere poetic, conventional standard. We find, for example, the followers of an Anglo-Saxon lord called Hringstan, who had earned the displeasure of Offa of Mercia, in exile with their leader in the Frankish kingdom; Charles the Great interceded to recover for them a position in their native land after their lord was dead.[4] Such men would have concurred very readily

---

[1] Ibid., pp. 12 f.
[2] See F. M. Stenton, *Anglo-Saxon England*, p. 299.
[3] *Vita S. Guthlaci*, pp. 42, 46 f.   [4] *Alcuini Epistolae*, p. 128.

in Wiglaf's scornful reproaches to the retainers who
failed to come to Beowulf's help in his need.[1] Yet it was
not only unfaithful followers who could find themselves
in the unhappy position with which Wiglaf threatens
the deserters: the death or defeat of a prince might
leave his followers destitute. In the latter part of the
eighth century our evidence shows that the amount of
civil war in Northumbria put many men in this position, and Alcuin blames Archbishop Eanbald II of York
for taking too many of them into his service; his pity for
them was causing him to travel with so large a comitatus
that he was heavily burdening the monasteries which
owed him hospitality.[2] The gloomy prognostications of
the messenger in *Beowulf* of the troubles likely to accrue
to the Geats from the death of their king[3] would have
seemed natural enough to the men of the poet's time.
They would not have thought, with some modern
scholars, that this anticipation of disaster casts doubt on
the historicity of Beowulf's successful reign. It may be
that Beowulf can be shown to be an unhistorical
character for other reasons; but sudden calamity
following a long and successful reign can easily be
paralleled from historical records. Within two years of
the death of Athelstan in 939 the English had to yield
up the whole of the reconquered Danelaw right as far
as Watling Street, and the death of Edgar the Peaceful in 975 was followed by some very unhappy years.
Yet these kings had reigned with outstanding success.
Alcuin wrote in 796 'the death of kings is the sign of

[1] ll. 2864–91.   [2] *Alcuini Epistolae*, p. 378.   [3] ll. 2900–3027.

misery',[1] and the messenger in *Beowulf* was of the same mind.

The audience would doubtless consist both of veterans and of young men. The former were men who had been given an establishment of their own, like Benedict Biscop, who began his career as a thegn of King Oswiu of Northumbria, and was given by him an estate by the time he had reached the age of twenty-five.[2] Youths grew up quickly in those days. Guthlac began his warlike career at the age of fifteen.[3] The men who had been thus rewarded were not in continuous attendance on their lord; they would be expected to flock to his standard in time of war, to his councils in peace, and probably to spend part of the year in his retinue. King Alfred reorganized his court so that his thegns might attend him in regular rotation, each serving for a third of the year.[4] The young men, on the other hand, would be brought up at their lord's court until such time as he saw fit to reward them with land on which they could settle. This is implied by a passage in which Bede expresses his fear that overlavish donations of land for supposed religious purposes will denude the king of the estates with which to reward his young followers, and that this will result in their taking service with other kings when they are thus prevented from marriage and setting up an establishment at home;

[1] *Alcuini Epistolae*, p. 171.
[2] Bede, *Historia Abbatum*, ed. Plummer, op. cit., i. 364 f.
[3] *Vita S. Guthlaci*, pp. 13 f.
[4] *Asser's Life of King Alfred*, ed. W. H. Stevenson (Oxford, 1904), pp. 86 f.

Northumbria will in this way be deprived of her natural
defenders.[1]

It seems likely that this same distinction is what is
meant by the poetic contrast between *duguð* 'body of
(tested) retainers' and *geoguð* 'youth'. Hrothgar's court
contained both groups, and besides them there were
folctogan 'chiefs of the people' who were not living at
court. These came 'from far and near' to look on
Grendel's arm, when the news of the hero's victory
reached them.[2] They were probably those members of
the *duguð* who were at home on their estates, and not in
attendance on the king. It seems to be suggested in the
Finn episode that many of Finn's followers scattered to
their homes when the fight was over, the treaty made,
and the obsequies for the fallen ended.[3] As in reality,
so in the poem, the king's thegns possess, or hope to
possess later on, *londriht* 'rights in land', for Wiglaf
includes these in his enumeration of the things forfeited
by the men who failed Beowulf.[4] One is reminded of
Ine's law (cap. 51) by which a nobleman who neglects
military service is to forfeit his land as well as to pay a
fine of 120 shillings. Wiglaf had himself received by
King Beowulf's gift the estates and residence and all
the rights which his father had held before him,[5] and
land formed part of the rich reward given by King
Hygelac to Eofor and Wulf when they had killed in
battle his enemy the Swedish king Ongentheow.[6] The

[1] *Epistola Bede ad Ecgbertum Episcopum*, ed. Plummer, op. cit., i. 415.
[2] ll. 837–40.   [3] ll. 1125–7.   [4] ll. 2884–90.
[5] ll. 2606–8.   [6] ll. 2991–5.

grant which King Hygelac made to Beowulf after his triumphant return from Denmark seems rather to be the cession of a province to his rule than a grant of estates; it consisted of 'seven thousand, a hall and a princely throne',[1] and has been compared with the 'three thousand of land' which Cenwealh of Wessex gave to his kinsman Cuthred in 648.[2] If the unexpressed unit of calculation in both these instances is the hide, the grant must certainly imply a sub-kingdom or an earldom, and it is worth noting that seven thousand hides is the assessment of no fewer than six of the peoples mentioned in the Tribal Hidage.[3] It occurs also in Bede, as the figure for North Mercia, and it was probably regarded as a normal assessment for a moderately large province.

Though young men in the king's service hope some day to be given land on which to support themselves and raise a family, this does not mean that they are indifferent meanwhile, or indeed at any time, to valuable gifts of armour or jewellery which may make them 'ever afterwards the more honoured on the mead-bench',[4] and which can be handed down as treasured heirlooms. The ceremonious giving of such things is a favourite subject of poetry, but it is not in this alone that generosity is extolled as an essential virtue in a king, and chroniclers do not omit to tell us when kings 'made great gifts of money' or 'made gifts in royal fashion' to

---

[1] ll. 2195 f. [2] Anglo-Saxon Chronicle, s.a.
[3] See H. M. Chadwick, *Studies on Anglo-Saxon Institutions*, p. 264.
[4] Cf. ll. 1901 f.

visitors to their courts. Objects of very great value are often referred to in historical sources. For example, a tenth-century ealdorman speaks of 'the sword which King Edmund gave me, of a hundred and twenty mancuses of gold and having four pounds of silver on the belt',[1] and we hear also of diadems of a hundred and twenty mancuses of gold, and bracelets of eighty mancuses, and so on. These things become more impressive if one takes into consideration the high purchasing power of the precious metals in Anglo-Saxon times: six sheep or one ox could be bought for a mancus of gold, forty-eight sheep or eight oxen for a pound of silver. Such was the prestige given by the possession of objects of value that a legal treatise finds it necessary to state that to have a helmet, a coat-of-mail and a gold-plated sword is not in itself enough to entitle a man to the status of a thegn. If he has not five hides of land, he remains a *ceorl*, for all this grand equipment.[2] We can hardly wonder, therefore, that it should be in describing choice weapons and armour that the poet most often goes into detail. His audience would be interested in such things; and indeed, some surviving Anglo-Saxon metal-work is handsome enough to tempt a poet to linger over its description.

The Anglo-Saxon upper classes were fond of hunting and fowling. Hunting rights are often expressly mentioned in documents dealing with the transfer of land,

---

[1] D. Whitelock, *Anglo-Saxon Wills* (Cambridge, 1930), p. 6.
[2] *Norðleoda Laga*, chap. 10, ed. F. Liebermann, *Die Gesetze der Angelsachsen* (Halle, 1903), i. 460.

and obligations connected with these pastimes, such as affording hospitality to huntsmen and fowlers, feeding dogs and falcons, erecting fences for the hunt, often formed part of the service by which land was held. Men were willing to go to great trouble and expense to procure dogs, hawks, and falcons: we even find a king of Kent writing to the missionary St. Boniface in Germany to ask him to procure falcons of a special kind, capable of attacking cranes.[1] Stag-hunting, boar-hunting, and hawking are mentioned in *Beowulf*, and we should remember that when the poet relates how the hero shot the nicker with his javelin, he is addressing an audience of sportsmen.[2] What his hearers did not want to hear about was the humdrum routine of their daily life. We need not go to the poetry in the hope of learning how the aristocracy administered their estates, attended folk-moots, kept their households out of mischief, tracked their stolen cattle, performed other legal duties, and fulfilled their obligations to the Church. If the poet had chosen to tell us how much money Hrothgar paid as a wergild for Hondscioh,[3] or how the land granted to Wiglaf, Wulf, and Eofor was assessed, we might be in a slightly better position for locating the poem. But poetry is not interested in such prosaic details, and no local peculiarities can be distinguished in the way men fought their battles or drank their mead, or in any of the practices which the poem depicts.

[1] *S. Bonifatii et Lullii Epistolae* (Mon. Germ. Hist., Epistolae Selectae, i), ed. M. Tangl, p. 231; translated by E. Kylie, *The English Correspondence of Saint Boniface* (London, 1911), p. 157.
[2] ll. 1425–41.
[3] ll. 1053–5.

What we are told in the poem suggests that there is
no contradiction between the conditions mirrored there
and those of England in the days of the Heptarchy, as
far as these are known, except for the retention of earlier
burial rites. I see nothing, apart from these, to indicate
that the poet is writing in an antiquarian vein, trying to
reconstruct a former age. His Danish court is held in a
city, for its inhabitants are called *ceaster*-dwellers, a term
which originally referred to towns of Roman origin,
though it may have become generalized; its streets are
paved,[1] the floor of the king's hall is tesselated,[2] and its
walls hung, at any rate on great occasions, with gold-
woven hangings,[3] perhaps of a material similar to that
of purple woven with gold which vested the altar of
Wilfrid's church at Ripon,[4] or to that 'of remarkable
purple interwoven everywhere with gold in the fashion
of a breast-plate', of which a *chlamys* of King Edgar
was made.[5] The hall itself was gold-adorned, and it
gleamed from a distance.[6] Remembering what Bede
has to say of the state upheld by King Edwin of Northumbria, and what Sutton Hoo has taught us of the
wealth at the disposal of some East Anglian royalty,
I would hesitate to say that such magnificence was not
possible in the seventh century; but it was certainly no
less possible in the eighth. It shows at least that the poet

[1] l. 320.   [2] l. 725.   [3] ll. 994–6.
[4] *The Life of Bishop Wilfrid by Eddius Stephanus*, chap. xvii, ed. B. Col-
grave (Cambridge, 1927), pp. 36 f.
[5] *Liber Eliensis*, ed. D. J. Stewart (Anglia Christiana Soc., London,
1848), i. 160.
[6] ll. 307–11.

is not describing the conditions of heathen Denmark. But our poet would indeed be an unusual person if he were possessed of a sense of historic propriety, and tried to describe consistently what no longer existed, instead of the scenes with which he was familiar.

And now, perhaps, I may be allowed to indulge in speculation on how the poet wished to affect these men, and to consider why he chose for his central subject a story of monster-slaying, using heroic stories merely as illustration or as background. It is no longer usual for scholars to spend time regretting that he did so, or accusing him of a perverted sense of proportion. He was composing for men of his own day, and he doubtless had good reason for his choice of theme. Nor is it likely that it was forced on him because all the good 'historical' themes had been used up. His main story would be as real to his audience as would have been an account of the strife for the Danish throne among the members of the Scylding dynasty; and in the course of it, the poet has placed the race of monsters in relationship to a Christian universe, and has shown that they can be overcome by human beings of courage and fortitude who fight them with faith in God. He has shown that humanity is not left helpless in the hands of the evil powers. That was no trivial theme to the men of that day.

Yet one may wonder why he was so concerned that his hearers should at the same time have present in their minds certain stories about human conflicts. It was not, however, unusual for allusions to such stories to be introduced to enrich a theme. Even the small fragments which are all that is left of the *Waldere* poem—a work which, if it told the full story as known from other sources at the leisurely pace of these fragments, must have been little shorter than *Beowulf*—include references in passing to the tales of Weland and Theodric; while in the short poem *Deor* allusions to heroic legends are used to point a general moral. In *Beowulf* such references add dignity and solidity to the central theme: it was not just any hall that was haunted, it was a splendid royal hall, famous in story; it was no vague and nebulous region which the dragon ravaged, but one inhabited by a mighty people, who had played their part in stirring events. Nevertheless, the so constant reminder of these things makes one doubt if this is an adequate explanation of their presence. Perhaps there is more to it than that.

I do not, however, believe that the poet's intention was to pander to his audience's taste, in that he expected it to be more interested in human histories of the clash of personalities, of the conflict between ambition and duty, between affection and duty, between conflicting duties; nor that he was himself irresistibly drawn to such subjects and thus inserted references to them on the slightest provocation. If this were so, why should he have failed to emphasize similar situations in his hero's career? What was Beowulf's dilemma when his lord and kinsman Heardred was killed by the Swedish king, Onela? He could, presumably, have raised the forces of his own province and brought them, to inevitable defeat, against the whole Swedish host; or he could come to terms and bide his time, though it meant accepting a kingdom from the slayer of his lord, and surely that would involve an oath of allegiance. He accepted the kingdom, but later he supported a rival of King Onela and helped to kill him, thus avenging his lord Heardred. The poet was eager to present a similar dilemma in the case of Hengest, but he skates over it hastily in his hero's life, so hastily that one hardly notices it. He simply says that Onela 'let Beowulf hold the throne and rule the Geats'.[1]

The poet must deliberately have refrained from enlarging on this incident. To have done so would have been to spoil a contrast which, I think, he is making: not a contrast between unreal adventures and realistic stories, but one between noble, disinterested deeds for the good of the human race and actions of violence and passion, arising from divided loyalties, or, worse still, from ambition and treachery. The tales he recalls are well known to his audience, but perhaps he is putting an unusual type of emphasis on them, stressing the suffering caused to innocent persons rather than the triumph of successful warfare and vengeance. Maybe he is asking: 'What would Hildeburh have said of the way in which the retainers of Hnæf "repaid the shining mead"?'[2] Their loyalty cost her a son, a husband, and a home. And did not Hygelac bring disaster on his

---

[1] ll. 2389 f.

[2] *Finnsburg*, ll. 39 f.; *hwitne* 'white, shining' is sometimes emended to *swetne* 'sweet'.

people when he made his celebrated Rhineland raid, attacking 'out of pride' a people with whom he was not at war? There must, however, be no uncertainty about the beneficent effect of Beowulf's deeds; hence the poet does not care to emphasize a situation in his career that puts him on a level with the characters of heroic legend.

Besides providing a foil of this kind to the main events, the sub-themes have another result. The poet seems determined not to let us forget how temporary are the effects even of good actions in this world. Heorot is freed from Grendel, only to witness the destruction of the Scylding dynasty through the evil passions of its members; Beowulf ruled his people well and saved them from the dragon, but foreign enemies lie in wait to pounce on them and destroy them once their king is dead. It is this which has caused the poem to be called pessimistic. It is full of the sense of the temporal nature of all earthly success. But the hero lived his life so that the final words of the poem can claim: 'Of the kings of the world, he was the mildest of men and the gentlest, the kindest to the people, and the most eager for fame'— words which remind us of what King Alfred said in his *Boethius*: 'I desired to live worthily as long as I lived, and to leave after my life to the men who should come after me my memory in good works.'[1] Beowulf had taken Hrothgar's advice and chosen the *ece rædas*.[2] Seen in relation to the things which last for ever the poem is not pessimistic.

[1] *King Alfred's Old English Version of Boethius*, ed. W. J. Sedgefield (Oxford, 1899), p. 41.   [2] ll. 1758–60.

There were certain periods in Anglo-Saxon history
when pessimism in relation to temporal affairs must have
been particularly easy: Bede found his times difficult;
Alcuin writes of his: 'Times of tribulation are everywhere in our land.'[1] Yet there was certainly never any
period when it would have been unlikely that a poet,
whose temperament inclined him that way, would stress
the transitoriness of earthly happiness and success. I
am sceptical about attempts to date the poem from its
general tone, and to attribute it to a period of greatness,
or else of decline. It may be that a certain modicum of
stable government was necessary before an artistic work
on this scale would be undertaken; and perhaps it
would not have been tactful to harp so much on the
greatness of kings who made all their neighbours subject
to them, if the poet were composing for a people who
had lost their independence to a foreign overlord. But
I doubt whether much weight should be attached to
general arguments of this nature. Nevertheless, if even
a few of the claims I have made are true, we must
suppose a subtle and sophisticated poet, and an alert
and intelligent audience, and it will therefore be in
place to conclude by showing that this was not impossible even at a later period than 'the age of Bede'.

A little before the year 700 all England had been
won, nominally, to Christianity, but it is to the eighth
century that one must assign much of the steady, un-
spectacular advance which brought a deeper knowledge of the faith to the ordinary layfolk all over the

[1] *Alcuini Epistolae*, p. 179.

land, by the gradual establishment of parish churches and the provision of a permanent income for the Church. Missionary zeal in the eighth century was free to turn abroad, and the upper classes, at any rate, over all England followed the work of the missionaries on the Continent with great interest. The people of Northumbria appear to have felt a particular responsibility for the mission to the Frisians, which had been begun in the late seventh century by the Northumbrian Willibrord, and later for that to the Old Saxons. It was to York that young Frisians came to be educated in the mid-eighth century, and there also a bishop for the Old Saxons, called Aluberht, was consecrated in 767; a Northumbrian synod, under King Alhred, was responsible for sending Willehad, the later missionary to the Old Saxons, to Frisia between 766 and 774. Even in political concerns, the picture of unrelieved gloom in Northumbria in the eighth century can be overdrawn. It was, in fact, to the reign of Eadberht Eating (737–58) that later Northumbrian writers looked back as a golden age;[1] and even later, although civil wars between rival claimants to the throne were frequent, and deeds of treachery and violence no rarity, there were reigns in which kings ruled well, paying due attention to spiritual concerns. A ninth-century Latin poem, which tells the history of a Northumbrian monastery, by no means looks back on the eighth century as solely

[1] See Alcuin, *Carmen de Sanctis Eboracensis Ecclesiae*, ll. 1247–86; *Historia Dunelmensis Ecclesiae*, ed. T. Arnold, *Symeonis Monachi Opera*, i. 47–9.

a period of strife and disorder; on the contrary, it speaks
of the prosperity of this house and of the great gifts it
received from Northumbrian noblemen.[1] As regards
scholarship, Northumbria continued to be regarded
as one of the leading centres in Europe. It has not
hitherto been noted that it was in touch with the
Frankish court as early as the reign of Eadberht Eating, to whom King Pippin sent letters and gifts;[2] and
the bond with the Frankish kingdom was naturally
much strengthened after the Northumbrian scholar,
Alcuin, went on Charles the Great's invitation to take
charge of his palace school and direct his educational
reforms.

It is not surprising, therefore, that Carolingian influence should become visible in Northumbrian art,
eventually culminating in the great works such as the
Easby and Rothbury crosses. Art historians are inclined
to date these works at about the extreme limit of the
period I would allow for *Beowulf*, but Dr. Kendrick
admits that the period which saw, in his words, 'nothing
less than a re-awakening of the classically conceived
sculptural art' is only 'somewhat vaguely centred upon
the year 800'.[3] At least we can see that the North-
umbrians of the end of the eighth century were not
so sunk in political disturbances as to be totally un-
interested in other matters, but were alive to artistic

[1] *Carmen Æðelwulfi*, ed. T. Arnold, op. cit., i. 267–94, especially
chaps. xv, xx.

[2] *Historia Dunelmensis Ecclesiae*, loc. cit.

[3] T. D. Kendrick, *Anglo-Saxon Art to A.D. 900* (London, 1938), pp. 152,
158.

influences, and quick to respond to an impetus from outside. Nor was art dead in the intervening period, which separates the greatest work of the Hiberno-Saxon style, as at Bewcastle and Ruthwell, from the masterpieces in the new manner; impressive work of the traditional school was still being produced. Acca's cross, if it is Acca's cross, must be dated about 740, and illuminated manuscripts like the Durham Cassiodorus and the Echternach Gospels are usually assigned to the middle of this century. Moreover, Northumbria maintained its contacts with the Celtic lands; intercourse with Ireland was facilitated by the continuance of an Anglo-Saxon see at Inishboffin off the coast of Mayo, and links with Iona were not permanently disrupted by the decision of the Synod of Whitby on the Easter question in 663. One learns incidentally of the visit of an abbot of Iona to Ripon in the middle of the eighth century.[1] I doubt whether, for the purpose of dating *Beowulf*, one can build securely on Professor Girvan's claim that 680–700 'was the period when Northumbria was at the height of its greatness politically and artistically; it was also the period when it was on the edge of decline'.[2] The decline was not so marked and so continuous as to make the later production of a great poem impossible, or even unlikely.

There is, however, no good reason for assigning the poem to Northumbria, and perhaps, if we had as much

[1] A note in the Chartres manuscript of the *Historia Brittonum*. See F. Lot, *Nennius et l'Historia Brittonum* (Bibliothèque de l'école des hautes études, fascicule 263, 1934), p. 29.

[2] *Beowulf and the Seventh Century*, p. 25.

evidence relating to the great age of Mercia as we have
for the great age of Northumbria, 'the age of Bede'
would lose some of its appeal for *Beowulf* scholars. But
there is no Mercian chronicle, there is no biographer of
Æthelbald or of Offa, and the laws of the latter king,
known to King Alfred and perhaps alluded to by
Alcuin when he speaks of 'the good, moderate and
chaste customs which Offa of blessed memory established',[1] have perished. Yet, in spite of the unsatisfactory
nature of the evidence, enough can be learnt from
charters and the correspondence with the missionaries
to show that Mercia had religious houses that were
centres of learning, and that its people were interested
in the spread of the Christian faith on the Continent.
The missionary Lul asks for a rare book from a bishop
of Worcester;[2] Alcuin sends a scholar to King Offa at
his request,[3] and corresponds with Mercian noblemen
and ladies. Politically, as we have seen, Mercia was the
leading kingdom in the eighth century, and in direct
contact with the court of Charles the Great. Its achievements included not only the lost laws of Offa, but also
that impressive monument, Offa's Dyke.

The evidence for the condition of the other English
kingdoms is not very full, but it can be seen that all
shared in the interest in foreign missions and the increased contact with the Continent which these occasioned. Kent, containing the metropolitan see, was on

---

[1] *Alcuini Epistolae*, p. 180.
[2] *S. Bonifatii et Lullii Epistolae*, p. 245.
[3] *Alcuini Epistolae*, p. 107.

this account and by its position on the shortest cross-Channel route much exposed to influence from abroad. It possessed, at Canterbury, a school with a long tradition behind it, and to this centre is attributed a style of manuscript illumination at about the middle of the eighth century, of which the Golden Gospels of Stockholm and the Vespasian Psalter are the best known examples. It is a style which combines classical feeling and some Merovingian motifs with the interlace and trumpet-patterns typical of the Hiberno-Saxon art of the North, thus illustrating in the sphere of art that political barriers did not prevent intercourse between the various kingdoms of the Heptarchy. We know from the references in letters to and from Boniface and Lul that book-production went on in the eighth century in the other southern kingdoms; their products are probably indistinguishable from those of Canterbury. Wessex was able to supply a number of well-educated men and women to the German missions in the early and mid-eighth century, and between 755 and 766, Bishop Cyneheard of Winchester asked his kinsman, the missionary Lul, to send him from the Continent any books he came across which Winchester had not already got, including books of secular knowledge, especially those on medical matters.[1] As for East Anglia, we know at least that Cuthwine, bishop of Dunwich from 716 to 731, was a collector of illuminated manuscripts,[2] and that King Ælfwald, who died in 749, commissioned

---

[1] *S. Bonifatii et Lullii Epistolae*, pp. 246 f.
[2] W. Levison, *England and the Continent in the Eighth Century*, p. 133.

Felix to write the Latin *Life of St. Guthlac*. In short, it would be unsafe to argue that any part of England was in the eighth century insufficiently advanced in intellectual attainments for a sophisticated poem like *Beowulf* to have been composed there and appreciated.

INDEX

Abel, 5, 7.

Acca's cross, 102.

accidental slaying, 15, 18.

Ælfwald, k. of East Anglia, 29, 104.

— k. of Northumbria, 29.

Æthelbald, k. of Mercia, 29, 32, 87, 103.

Æthelnoth, biographer of St. Cnut, 61.

Æthelweard, chronicler, 38.

Æthelwulf, k. of Wessex, 33 n.

— Latin poet, 100 f.

Alcuin, 13, 20, 25 f., 32, 37, 49, 87 n., 88, 99–101, 103.

Aldfrith, k. of Northumbria, 20, 29.

Aldhelm, St., 33.

Aldred, earl of Northumbria, 16–18.

Alfred, k. of Wessex, 26, 33, 89, 98, 103; his *Boethius*, 98

Alhred, k. of Northumbria, 29, 100.

Aluberht, bishop of the Old Saxons, 100.

Ammianus Marcellinus, 39.

Angel, *see* Offa, k. of.

Anglian crosses, 29; *see* Acca's cross, Bewcastle, Easby, Rothbury, Ruthwell.

Anglo-Latin scholarship, 48.

Anketil, monk of St. Albans and moneyer to the k. of Denmark, 62.

Annales Ryenses, 60.

archaeological evidence, 82–5.

Athelstan, k. of England, 88.

Attoarii, *see* Hetware.

Augustine, St.: *City of God*, 48.

barrow, 75, 81 f.; in place-names, 73 f., 74 n.

Beaw (Beo), 70.

Bede, 9, 40, 85 f., 91, 94, 99; Letter to Archbishop Egbert, 21, 89; dating of *Beowulf* in age of, 22 f., 28 f., 99, 103.

Benedict Biscop, 7, 89.

Beowulf: date of, 4–30, 64, 82–5, 99–105; episodes in, 34–64, 95–8; homogeneity of, 4; localization of, 30–3, 63 f., 93; main theme of, 34, 64–70, 95 f.; manuscript of, 51 f.; oral recital of, 20 f.

Beowulf the Dane, 69 f.

Beowulf the Geat: funeral of, 84; historicity of, 88 f.; province of, 91, 96; rule of, 90, 97 f.

Bewcastle cross, 102.

biblical allusions, 5 f.

— commentaries, 5.

bigulfesburh (Belbury Castle), 66.

Biuulf, 66.

Bjarkamál, 36.

Blickling Homilies, 67 n.

blood-feud, 13–19, 71, 86.

Boniface, St., 25, 79, 93, 104.

Bowulf, 66.

Bretwalda, 32.

Brísinga men, 57.

Brosinga mene, 43, 56 f.

Caedmon, 9 f.

Cain, 5–7, 76 f., 79 f.

Cambridge Thanes' Guild, 14, 17.

candel, 6.

Carl, Thurbrand's son, 16–18.

ceaster, 94.

Cenred, k. of Mercia, 86.

Cenwealh, k. of Wessex, 91.

chamber-tomb, 81.

Charles the Great, 14, 32, 87, 101, 103.

charms, 75, 78.

charters, linguistic evidence of, 27 f., 33 n.

Chlochilaichus, *see* Hygelac.
Christian element in *Beowulf*, 3–12, 26, 71, 81 f., 95.
— phraseology in Old English poetry, 9–11, 21; translated from Latin, 10 f., 81.
Clofesho, synod of 747 at, 79.
Cnut, k. of England, 25, 61; laws of, 79 n.
— St., k. of Denmark, 61.
continental intercourse, 46, 48, 50, 61 f., 100–4.
conversion of the English, 5–7, 12, 21 f., 57, 99 f.
court of the king, organization of, 89–92.
Creation: hymn of, 9, 76 f., 81; monsters in relation to, 7, 76 f., 79 f., 95.
cremation, *see* funeral rites.
curse on buried treasure, 81 f.
Curtius, Quintus, 48.
Cuthred, 91.
Cuthwine, bishop of Dunwich, 104.
Cyneheard, bishop of Winchester, 104.
Cynewulf, k. of Wessex, 29, 32, 33 n.
— poetry of, 26, 28, 30.

Dæghrefn, 41, 44.
Danelaw, 15, 25 f., 88.
Danes, 24 f., 40, 42, 47, 49, 55, 61 f., 64 f., 78, 94; kings of, *see* Cnut, Frotho, Heremod, Scyldings, Waldemar.
Danish contacts with England, 61 f.
Deda, abbot of Partney, 85.
De gestis Caroli Magni, 45.
De Monstris et de Belluis, see *Liber Monstrorum*.
De obsessione Dunelmi, 16 n.
Deor, 96.
devil, the, 8, 10 f., 21, 77, 81; arrows of, 8, 80 f.
dragon, 10, 20, 34, 53, 55, 65, 69 f., 73–5, 81 f., 96, 98; in place-names, 73 f.

Drida, 59.
duguð, 90.
Durham MS. of Cassiodorus, 102.

Eadberht Eating, k. of Northumbria, 29, 100 f.
Eadgils, 65.
Eanbald II, archbishop of York, 88.
Easby cross, 101.
East Anglia, 87, 94, 104; k. of, *see* Ælfwald.
ecclesiastical attitude to poems, 19 f.
Echternach Gospels, 102.
Edgar, k. of England, 88, 94.
Edmund, k. of England, 92; laws of, 15.
Edward, cleric from St. Albans, in Denmark, 62.
Edwin, k. of Northumbria, 94.
Eider, River, 60, 63.
Ely, gospel-book from, 14.
entanhlew, 74.
Eofor, 90, 93.
Eormenric (Ermenrichus), 39, 56.

Felix, *see* Guthlac, St., Life of.
Finn, 18 f., 35, 37, 83, 90.
Finnsburg, 37, 97 n.
Fitela, 57.
Fleury, St. Benedict's Abbey, 48.
Flood, 5 f., 80.
folctogan, 90.
forscrifan, 6.
Frankish capitulary, 79.
— historians, 39–46, 54.
Franks (Hugas), 34, 41, 43 f., 46, 101; kings of, *see* Charles, Pippin, Theudebert, Theuderic.
Frisians, 43 f., 50, 100.
Frotho, k. of the Danes, 69 f.
funeral rites, 12, 22, 77, 82–6.

Geats, 34, 38 f., 42–4, 47, 49, 54 f., 65, 88, 97; kings of, *see* Beowulf, Hrethel, Hygelac.
Genesis, 5, 7; Old Saxon poem, 79.
geoguð, 90.

Gesta Francorum, see *Liber Historiae Francorum*.
Getæ, 46.
giants, 5, 7; in place-names, 74.
Gnomic Poem, 75.
gold-woven cloth, 94.
Gregory of Tours, 39–41, 45.
Grendel, 10 f., 53, 66, 72, 76, 81, 98; in place-names, 66, 74.
Grendel's mother, 11, 20, 66, 68 f.
Grettissaga, 65, 67.
Guthlac, St., Life of, 27, 29, 75, 80–2, 86 f., 89, 105; poems on, 27, 80.

Haeha (Hean), abbot, 27.
Ham, son of Noah, 79.
Hama, 56.
hawking, 92 f.
Heardred, 96.
heathenism, 3, 11 f., 13, 21, 26, 77–9, 81 f., 85.
Heathobards, 36, 71.
Heliand, 6.
Hengest, 17 f., 97.
Heorot, 9, 64, 66, 71, 81, 98.
Hcorowcard, 36 f.
Heremod, 98.
Hetware (Attoarii), 41, 44–6.
Hildeburh, 35, 97.
Historia Brittonum, 102 n.
Hnæf, 18, 97.
Hnauggvanbaugi, 36 n.
homiletic tradition, 7 f.
Hondscioh, 93.
Hrabanus Maurus, 49.
Hrethel, 18, 54.
Hrethric, 35 f.
Hringstan, 87.
Hrolfs Saga Kraka, 64 f.
Hrothgar, 9, 35, 37, 56, 76, 78, 81, 93, 98.
Hrothulf (Rudolphus), 36–8.
Hugas, see Franks.
Hug-Dietrich, 45.
Huglecus, 54.
Hugleikr, 54.
Hunlaf (Hunlapus), 38.
hunting, 92 f.

Hygd, 58 f.
Hygelac (Chlochilaichus), 38–56, 58, 90 f., 97.

Ine, k. of Wessex, 29, 90.
Ingeld, 17, 20, 26, 37, 50, 71.
Inishboffin, Anglo-Saxon see at, 102.
intercourse between kingdoms, 31, 104.
Iona, 102.
Isidore of Seville, 48, 52.

John of St. Albans, 62.

Kent, 21, 29, 93; conditions in, 87, 103 f.; k. of, see Wihtred.

land, grants of, 89–91.
Langfeðgatal, 36 n.
Latin loan-words, 5 f.
law, Anglo-Saxon, 15 f., 17 f., 21 n., 79 n., 90, 92.
Letter of Alexander to Aristotle, 51 f.
Liber Historiae Francorum, 41, 45.
Liber Monstrorum, 42, 46–53, 71; Leyden MS. of, 47 f.
Liber Vitae of Lindisfarne, 66.
Lindisfarne, 20, 37; Gospels, 29; *Liber Vitae*, 66.
linguistic evidence, 26–8, 30 f., 33.
literacy of the laity, 19 f.
londriht, 90.
loyalty to a lord, 13, 87 f., 97.
Lucan, 48.
Lucas, secretary to Christopher of Denmark, 62 n.
Lul, 103 f.

manuscript illumination, 29, 102, 104.
Marcellinus Comes, 48.
Marvels (or Wonders) of the East, 51 f.
material standards of living, 94 f.
Mercia: conditions in, 86 f., 103; supremacy of, 32 f.; kings of, see Æthelbald, Cenred, Offa.

Merovingian, 44, 49; influence, 104.

minstrels, 9, 31, 35, 76 f., 81.

missions to the Continent, 50, 100, 103 f.

Modþryð, 58.

monsters, 7, 24, 34 f., 46–53, 64–9, 71–80; origin of, 7, 76 f., 79 f., 95.

New Testament: absence of reference to, 6 f.; pictures illustrating, 7.

Nicholas of St. Albans, 62.

nicor, 93; in place-names, 74.

non, 6.

Norðleoda Laga, 92 n.

Northumbria: conditions in, 21 f., 29, 32, 86, 88, 100–2; religious poetry of, 31; earls of, *see* Aldred, Siward, Waltheof; kings of, *see* Ælfwald, Aldfrith, Alhred, Eadberht Eating, Edwin, Oswiu.

occupations of the nobility, 86–93.

Odense, Denmark, 61.

Odo, treasurer of King Waldemar, 62.

Offa, k. of Angel, 31, 58–64.

— k. of Mercia, 29, 32 f., 59, 61, 63 f., 87, 103.

Offa's Dyke, 63, 103.

Old Saxons; mission to, 100; bishops of, *see* Aluberht, Willehad; poetry of, *see* Genesis, *Heliand*.

Old Testament: references to, 6 f.; pictures illustrating, 7.

Onela, 65, 96 f.

Ongentheow, 90.

Oswiu, k. of Northumbria, 89.

Paulinus, 85.

Peterborough, daughter-houses of, 31.

Physiologus, 48.

Pippin, k. of the Franks, 101.

place-name evidence, 66, 72–5.

puca, *pucel*, in place-names, 72, 74.

religious poetry, 8–11, 21, 31.

Ripon, 94, 102.

Roller, 54.

Rome, pilgrimage to, 17.

Rothbury cross, 101.

Ruthwell cross, 102.

St. Albans, 59–62.

Saxo Grammaticus, 54, 60, 62, 63 n., 69.

Scandinavian sources, 26, 36 f., 54, 57, 60 f., 64–6, 69.

Scedenig (*Sconeg*), 26.

Scef, 38.

scinna, 73; in place-names, 73.

scucca, 73, 74 n.; in place-names, 73.

Scyld, 12, 38, 69 f., 83 f.

Scyldings, 34–8, 64 f., 95, 98.

segen, 83.

Seth, 5.

Settrington, 17.

ship-burial, *see* funeral rites.

ships, 84.

Sigemund, 57.

Siward *Digri*, earl of Northumbria, 70.

skratti, O.N., 74 n.

Stockholm, Golden Gospels of, 104.

Sutton Hoo, 22, 83–5, 94.

Swedes, 34, 54 f., 97; kings of, *see* Eadgils, Onela, Ongentheow.

Sweyn Aageson, chronicle of, 60.

Theodric (the Ostrogoth), 96.

Theudebert, k. of the Franks, 40, 45.

Theuderic (Theodric), k. of the Franks, 40, 45 f.

Þidrekssaga, 56.

Thryth, 58–60.

Thurbrand, 16.

þyrs, 72, 73 n., 75; in place-names, 72 f.

Torhtmund, 14.

treasure: grants of, 91 f.; value of, 92.

Tribal Hidage, 91.
tumulus, *see* barrow.

Ulysses, Greek picture of, 53.

vendetta, *see* blood-feud.
Vercelli homily, 8.
Vespasian D. iv, 38.
Vespasian Psalter, 104.
Vésteinn, 55 n.
Viking Age, 24–6, 78.
Virgil, 48 f.
Visio S. Pauli, 67 and n.
Vita et Passio Waldevi, 70 n.
Vitae duorum Offarum, 59 f.
Volsungasaga, 57 n.

Waldemar the Great, k. of Den-
    mark, 62; his son Waldemar, 62.
Waldere, 96.
Walthcof, earl of Northumbria,
    17.
Wealhtheow, 35, 43, 78.

Weland, 96.
Weohstan, 55.
wergild, 13 f., 16, 18, 93.
Wessex, 30, 38; conditions in, 87,
    104; kings of, *see* Æthelwulf,
    Alfred, Cenwealh, Cynewulf,
    Ine.
Whitby, Synod of, 102.
Widsith, 37 f., 46, 55, 60, 63 f.
Wiglaf, 34, 55, 88, 90, 93.
Wihtred, k. of Kent, 21 n.
Wilfrid, St., 22, 94; Eddius's Life
    of, 94 n.
Willehad, 100.
Willibrord, 100.
Wolf-Dietrich, 45.
Wonders of the East, see *Marvels*, &c.
Wulf, 90, 93.
Wulfstan II, bishop of Worcester,
    15.
wyrm, in place-names, 74.

Ynglingassaga, 54.
Ywaine and Gawin, 80.

PRINTED IN
GREAT BRITAIN
AT THE
UNIVERSITY PRESS
OXFORD
BY
CHARLES BATEY
PRINTER
TO THE
UNIVERSITY

ALL THE PAINTINGS OF
GIORGIONE

VOLUME THREE
in the
Complete Library of World Art

The Complete Library of World Art

ALL THE PAINTINC

F GIORGIONE

Text *by* LUIGI COLETTI
Translated by PAUL COLACICCHI

HAWTHORN BOOKS, INC.

Publishers · New York

Printed in Great Britain by
Jarrold and Sons Ltd, Norwich

CONTENTS

	page
GIORGIONE, LIFE AND WORK	7
BIOGRAPHICAL NOTES	37
GIORGIONE'S PAINTINGS	39
PAINTINGS ATTRIBUTED TO GIORGIONE	53
WORKS MENTIONED IN EARLY SOURCES	58
LOCATION OF PAINTINGS	63
SELECTED CRITICISM	66
BIBLIOGRAPHICAL NOTE	77
REPRODUCTIONS	79

GIORGIONE

Life and Work

VERY little is known definitely about Giorgione. It is certain that he died young, at the age of thirty-three or thirty-four, in Venice during the plague in the autumn of 1510; that he had gone to Venice from the countryside near Treviso, more precisely from Castelfranco in the immediate neighborhood; that in 1507–8 he received many important commissions; that after his death the most sophisticated collectors were competing for his works, while other painters were busily turning out imitations of his pictures. For this reason, there was a sudden confusion in attributions between Giorgione's paintings and those by other contemporary artists, especially Titian.

Upon these few known facts the legend was built: that he was born into the noble family of Barbarella (which is possible but not proved); that he was jealous of other painters and particularly of Titian; that he loved music, and had many love affairs.

Forty years after his death Vasari wrote a profile of the master, placing him in a perspective which made later Venetian critics conclude that not only was there a parallel to be drawn between Giorgione and Leonardo da Vinci, but that the former had very much the same influence upon modern painting, as we understand it today, in the Veneto, as Leonardo had on Tuscan painting.

Giorgione's "Leonardismo" was not accepted by Boschini or Lanzi; but a recent school of thought, headed by Hourticq and Suida, and rejected by L. Venturi and Fiocco, would replace Giorgione by Titian as the reformer of Venetian art, and would present Giorgione on the exclusive basis of the information given by M. A. Michiel, who was almost a contemporary of his. The author feels, however, that Michiel's facts do not invalidate Vasari's presentation.

Giorgione's language and poetry, his *ratio videndi* and *ratio pingendi*, which we shall strive to define from the group of paintings definitely attributed to him, can be based upon three pictures universally recognized as his work: *The Castelfranco Madonna* (plates 42–46), *The Three Philosophers* (plates 48–53) and the *Gypsy and Soldier* (plates 54–60). In fact, the *Gypsy and Soldier* would suffice, since there can be no doubt about its authorship. We may even dispense from using as a term of reference the *Sleeping Venus* (plates 68–71), which the author ascribes to Giorgione, although others do not.

Binocular vision has by now become such a part of our experience that we no longer realize its admirable complexity, which appears to grip reality in a vice. It is due to the super-imposition and the blending of two similar impressions that we can see an object concretely, in all its relief.

Contrarily, as the object moves away from us the angle of vision become narrower, until it vanishes—theoretically *ad infinitum*, but practically long before that—when the rays, having become parallel, no longer produce a three dimensional effect since the two images can no longer blend. At that point all sense of relief will disappear.

Similarly, for those who use only one eye, the shadows

upon a hillside do not help to define every detail of the surface in relation to the source of light, so that, while they may see the volume of the hillside against the plain, it will appear completely flat. In other words, it will no longer have a plastic function, but merely a chromatic one. An image, therefore, as it moves away from the eye, will lose in weight, in thickness and in detail, but at the same time it will gain in lightness, in transparency and in universality. What vision loses in tactile potentiality, it gains in chromatic possibilities in an equal measure. All these facts had been partially noticed and recorded by Leonardo da Vinci, but other artists had also understood them, and had even translated them into pictorial terms. Let us mention Michelangelo, for instance, and consider the small nude figures in the background of the Doni tondo. They are the result of a few quick transparent touches of the brush; their plastic value is extremely limited if compared with the very elaborate modeling of the foreground group. They prove that the painter was essentially a sculptor, and therefore dominated by plastic interests. He could see and represent distant figures as pure color, devoid of all plasticity. For him, the only function of that particular background was to stress the effect of relief and increase the solidity of the figures in the foreground.

The secret of Giorgione was merely that he saw the whole spectacle of the world as a non-tangible but exclusively visible distance. He reduced the whole of his representation to "pure color". This is the moment when painting becomes really and only painting, giving up all claims to emulate or simulate sculpture or, worse still, to offer an equivalent rather than an image of reality. From this moment the Renaissance's ambiguous and illusive formula of the imitation of nature was superseded. For Renaissance artists color and movement had, of course, some value—let us recall Vasari's insistence upon the merits of painting the "breath of life and warmth of human flesh"—but their main preoccupation was still with third dimensional representation.

Vasari, however, acknowledged the novelty of Giorgione's position on the technical side when he recorded that Giorgione used to paint directly with color, without first drawing the entire composition on the panel, as he was convinced that this was "the real and indeed the best way of drawing". Naturally, Vasari deplored this method, and even saw in it the root of all the evils which he imputed to the Venetian painters.

Obviously there were points of contact, reciprocal influences and limited coincidences between the Florentine and the Venetian schools. I think, however, that one should stress the fundamental and traditional distinction between the mainly plastic interest of the former and the pictorial eminence of the latter.

There was, in fact, a radical difference in the two methods of creating images. While the Florentines, on the one hand, based their representation upon volumetric assessment and considered color merely as an accessory, the Venetians began by conceiving an initial chromatic impression to which they then added muscle and bone. The former used chiaroscuro as a starting point, the latter color. These two methods have been described by Cennini in Chapter 67 of his *Trattato*: here the first one is called "the good method" and the second one "the method used by those who know little about art".

For the Venetians, therefore, all graphic preparation such as drawing, which for the Tuscans was the essential foundation of the image, was reduced to the function of a mnemonic aid, a sort of topographical note for the coagulation of color. This, as related to Giorgione's circle, can be seen in the attributed panel, *The Finding of Romulus and Remus*, now in Frankfurt (plate 101). The graphic points of support, or landmarks, upon which the pictorial structure was to rest, are still visible, and it does not matter whether this was due to the painting being unfinished or to the erosion of time.

Da Vinci himself recommended that the use of preparatory sketches did not require the elements to be carefully finished. This, however, was not an encouragement to imprecision. Leonardo's sketches were often abbreviated and *sous-entendu*, but never evasive; indeed, as is clearly visible in some of his works which never went beyond the preparatory stage, they were always in the nature of a commitment. The *Circumscription*, the "respect for the boundary" imposed by Alberti is still ever present in Da Vinci's work as a precise suggestion of form.

After all, the two different and even contrasting directions taken by the Florentine and Venetian schools can be derived from the ancient distinction seen by Lysippus between representing men, objects and the world as one sees them and as they are, between appearance and essence and between contingency and substance. In other words, while, by the usual Florentine procedure, the image is born, lives and concludes itself in the imagination, though still under the constant control of the intellect, the Venetian's imagination seems rather to play upon the senses. This does not mean that the latter is tantamount to automatism, but rather that the Venetian's research moves away from a mathematical consideration of reality's volumetric structure, toward the immediate assumption of reality, in its visible appearance; a rigorous perspective construction gives way to a tonal composition.

Did Giorgione's contemporaries immediately realize the revolutionary implications and the formidable consequences of the master's innovation? Was Venice divided, then and there, between the young and the old, between the progressive and the traditional schools? For this was not a normal evolution of taste, from one generation to another, but a sudden crisis.

To answer these questions we must know something of Venice's artistic position at that time.

That Giorgione started the modern manner in the Veneto, as Da Vinci did in Tuscany and Correggio in Lombardy, is clearly stated by Vasari, and there seems to be no reason for disbelieving him. The facts he relates were fairly recent for him, and yet not so recent that he could not see them in a historical perspective. Even allowing for his undeniable partiality of taste, one cannot deny that he was intelligent and a man of subtle judgement. It is also certain that the young elements of Venice now followed Giorgione as fifty years before in Padua they had followed Mantegna. Even Titian, if one accepts what Vasari and Dolce have written, became a convert to the youth from Castelfranco. The traditionalists resisted, but they were not very numerous, and when Giorgione died at a very early age, he had become the idol of Venice, whose taste he had reformed, particularly in the higher spheres of cultured society. This was due not only to the novelty of his content—the themes he chose, the spectacles he invented—but also to his new pictorial language, which had been immediately understood. The famous correspondence between Isabella d'Este and Francesco Albano testifies to the frenzied search for his works by collectors after his death. Giorgione brought a revolution to Venice, but a peaceful and timely one, rich with positive values, and prepared for by remarkable precedents.

Just when young Giorgione, having studied in the Bellinis' workshops, began his own career, an event of paramount importance occurred in Venice: Leonardo da Vinci paid a brief visit to the city in 1500.

Though Vasari does not mention it, this occurrence appears as the probable basis of a whole series of judgements which determine his critical attitude toward the last historical period of Italian painting: that third phase which Vasari calls the modern manner.

We have no records about the relationship between Da Vinci and Giorgione, but it is known that Da Vinci was called to Venice in 1500 by the Signoria for his advice on military matters, and it is extremely probable that he painted while there, or brought with him some paintings or drawings (perhaps the portrait of Isabella d'Este). Granting that the Venetians may not, at the time, have had direct experience with Da Vinci's painting, it seems unreasonable not to presume that Leonardo, who loved discourse, established contact with Venetian artistic circles and discussed professional problems with them, theorizing upon the optical density and upon the confused and hazy quality of distant objects, the optical phenomena, in other words, which he had been studying.

These problems of dispensing with outlines, and of "escaping from the profiles" were, after all, the same as had appealed to Giovanni Bellini, as a reaction against Mantegna's harshness, and induced him to attempt his first experiments in tonality. Da Vinci had solved the problem thanks to his discovery of *sfumato*, this being the exact translation, in pictorial language, of that density of air which in reality envelops all things, reducing to a common visual denominator the opaqueness of the surroundings and the volumes therein contained, the outlines of which disappear in the mass of the atmosphere. Da Vinci made great use of this technique to express the hazy quality of light in the evening hours. This is his "obscurity", a pictorial summary of surroundings, volumes, and dusk. The effect related to distance, the dispensing with outlines are obtained due to the lack of light. A conquest, the price of which is lack of color!

As far as Giorgione's obscurity is concerned, the validity of Vasari's assertion is proven by comparing the *Gypsy and Soldier* (plate 54) to Giovanni Bellini's *Giovanelli' Madonna* in the Accademia, Venice.

One will notice that the chromatic scale of the *Gypsy and Soldier* follows the opposite progression from that of the *Madonna*, in so far as it departs from a basis rich in color and charged with pigment, and therefore comparatively dark in the areas exposed to light, and then moves on to the shadows, where the hues are even deeper and darker. It is as though Bellini's colorful abstractions, the celestial transparencies of this last period, had found the core of a concrete chromatic substance. "Obscurity", therefore, but with a fullness of color at the same time.

That density of the air which Da Vinci the scientist recognized as universal, but which Da Vinci the artist could only express through penumbra, by sacrificing color, is achieved by Giorgione in terms of distance, thereby leaving intact the joy of color.

To represent the near objects as if they were distant, in other words emptied of tangible weight, means to resolve those objects in terms of pure color. But that color is graduated, because there is always, in air, a certain element of shadow blending with light, that veil in the night, which, however thin, will filter into the day. It is a shadow which not only falls on objects and gives them shape, but enfolds them and, in a sense, penetrates them.

At this point the thickening of darkness inside color, while on the one hand inserting into universal vision the evidence and the presence of the nearest objects, on the other reveals the exact measure of distances, so that the objects can be situated in their proper depth.

By these means distance becomes enriched with the closer experience; remoteness acquires propinquity; the substance and structure of things, the knowledge of the world are absorbed into its appearance.

One of the many aspects of this distant vision of Giorgione is the very scant interest shown by him in architectural scenography, which must be seen in "close-up".

We can almost imagine Vasari's patronizing smile as he wrote that to Giorgione's mind "painting directly with colors, without any attempt at preparatory drawing, was the real and the best way of drawing". These words, in fact, are immediately followed by an outburst in praise of drawing. But actually, the technical practice of painting with color alone, which requires the strictest discipline of one's sensitivity, presupposes a very important discovery: that color, while neither ignoring nor neglecting the laws of draftmanship and chiaroscuro, can transcend them, involving them in one single creative act.

It was actually Giorgione's poetic feeling for distance that revealed to him the new language and the best instrument for his aesthetic expression.

Having ascertained that Giorgione's technical interests coincided, at the start, with those of Leonardo, but then rapidly overtook them in a deeper, richer, and more complex interpretation of the world, we must now try to establish a clearer relationship between the two masters.

In 1490 the *Virgin of the Rocks* was completed, and by the beginning of 1498, *The Last Supper* was also completed. These were the years when Giorgione first began his professional activities, of which we know nothing definite. It seems reasonable to assume, aside from the works themselves, that fundamentally he liked to paint with colors alone. At the time of which we are speaking he must already have been so inclined. Da Vinci's arrival in Venice, in 1500, took place at a time when Giorgione, aged twenty-four, must already have shown some distinction, and may certainly have contributed toward throwing a theoretical light upon the technical problems that Giorgione had already solved in practice. Da Vinci's advice, in the author's opinion, should have played a great part in helping the younger painter to clarify his critical thinking and to formulate his own artistic language.

From this meeting Giorgione possibly acquired a greater assurance, a less self-conscious attitude, a bolder determination in his choice of shapes. This particular phase may perhaps have been recorded in the transition from the minute and almost weak compositions, in a style not unlike that of miniatures, rich with little chorus figures, to the more grandly composed works, in which the cast obeys a *mise en scène*. (See the three *Nativities* in plates 25, 30 and 33, and the *Castelfranco Madonna*, plate 42.)

Giorgione's poetic attitude also derived in part from his musical experience. This does not refer to his musical exercises upon which, from Vasari onwards, so many have insisted, and which would still have bound him closer to Da Vinci, but to his participation in musical circles which were particularly active in Venice at that time. Perhaps Raphael may have contributed toward forming his taste

16

through some engravings and drawings of his which were certainly known in Venice at the time. This has been remarked upon by many critics, and Raphael may well have inspired in Giorgione a classically serene and balanced vision of the world. On the other hand, the author cannot accept the many current assumptions that Giorgione was influenced by certain Northern painters and engravers, though it is possible that he occasionally borrowed from them some partial suggestions for motives.

The author also accepts, in principle, Ferriguto's conclusion that Giorgione was greatly interested in the literary culture of his time, though he cannot agree with that author's evaluation of the relationship between Giorgione and Da Vinci.

All these stimuli, and doubtless still others, combine to explain that constant transformation which is true of the life of every artist worthy of that name: life means change, both in the physical and in the material sense. To this constant transformation the artist himself contributes by reacting, positively or negatively, to his stimuli; by his own independent creative impulses; by reflection and exercise; and by the preparation and the execution of his works of art. In Giorgione's case, by training his own sensitivity to perceive, to measure and to define the ever subtler distinctions in chromatic relations.

This continuous inner formation is reflected in the concrete aspects of the work, the line of development of the artist's style, and the history of his artistic life.

Before attempting to trace this line of development, we must go back to that formative period of Giorgione's student days when he was learning both the grammatical and the manual rules of his future profession.

It would appear that his master was Giovanni Bellini, or both the Bellini brothers, or first Gentile, and then Giovanni. The latter is the most obvious version, considering Giambellino's position in Venice at the time when the youth arrived there from the Italian mainland where it is possible that he had learned, in some other workshop, the first rudiments of his craft and given signs of some promise.

Vasari, however, having indicated the goals that Giorgione hoped to achieve by studying and working with the Bellinis, adds immediately, "and by himself", a phrase which is significant.

Returning to the foundation of Giorgione's art, that is to say, to his poetical motive which can be summarized in his concept of distant vision: the pictorial language expressed by that approach and which involves the employment of pure color. This position is a radically new one, at least within the limitation of the artist's cultural experiences.

This new language of pure color seems so relevant, so necessary indeed to the representation of a new world of visual imagery, to the expression of that new poetic feeling, that one must regard it as a revelation to the artist in terms of a sudden illumination, as an idea pregnant with limitless development.

Surely Giorgione, as a boy, must have frequented artists' workshops; these were perhaps mediocre establishments on the mainland. He surely must have seen, in Venice, the works of Giovanni Bellini and have discovered, especially in the twenty-year-old paintings of that master, some latent tendency towards an interpretation of visual appearance very similar to his own. He must also have felt the affectionate humanity of Bellini's art, but let it be said that because of that same confidential tone both psychological and visual, which Bellini brought to his pictures, these contain only partial threads of *rapprochement* to the new use of color alone to express form. The ultimate secret eluded him, and only Giorgione could find it, with his *visione lontana*, the only vision which can reduce the visual world to pure color without a sense of omission.

Note how the two artists represent landscape. In the mature Giambellino it predominates so much that it almost becomes the subject of the painting, as for instance in the *St Francis* (New York, Frick Collection) and in the *Sacred Allegory* (Florence, Uffizi). These two works are magnificent for the fertility of their inventions and for the richness and variety of their episodes, but here and there they betray additions. The display of natural rural beauty by this inhabitant of the lagoon, who must have seen that beauty comparatively late in life, having spent his childhood in his city of stone, between the sky and the water, is equivalent to erudite complacency, so much so that one cannot avoid the feeling of artificiality, as in the case of an anthology of selected passages, which can never unite to form a poem.

From birth, Giorgione, the country lad from the mainland, had seen the great changing sky, tranquil in sunlight or torn asunder by storms over fields and meadows; he had seen the pattern made by the leaves against that sky, and the quiet nooks in the woods under little bridges; he had seen lazy, tortuous brooks weave their way through the grass or along ancient walls; he had seen the rolling hills and the ridged backs of mountains.

These sights, so familiar to mankind, appeared to him as providing the approach to the elemental and natural way of representing the inner essence of everything. They impressed themselves on his mind not so much as outward terms of reference, but as an inner guiding force. And this is why the landscapes, so copiously invented by his imagination—for they are even more imaginative than Giambellino's land-scapes—acquired such an intense and consistent quality of veracity and organic unity, as to appear spontaneously born, even if here and there the single details of his landscapes seem less faithful and more extravagant than those of Bellini. The most poetically fabulous aspects of Giorgione's work are perfectly credible, his dreams are endowed with a most persuasive realism.

Giorgione must also have studied and admired the paintings left in Venice, twenty years before, by Antonello da Messina, whom G. Fiocco considers to have provided the basis for, or certainly the most important stimulus to, the youth's artistic formation. Naturally, as Antonello left Venice at the time of Giorgione's birth, his influence could not have been a direct one. Also this influence was limited in that it could only consist of those aspects of Antonello's art which could appeal to Giorgione's artistic nature: referring specifically to those representations of distances in Antonello's *St Sebastian* and in the Antwerp *Crucifixion*, both admirable works for their balanced broadness, for their transparency and especially for the organized and simple clarity of their construction—this being most probably the legacy of Piero della Francesca.

While Giorgione was painting frescos on the façade of the newly rebuilt Fondaco dei Tedeschi (German Ware-house) in 1507–8, Fra Bartolomeo stayed in Venice, but his influence would appear to have been negligible compared with Giorgione's own study of the Ferrara School, and especially of Costa, Francia, and Benvenuto Tisi (called Garofalo).

Though the influence is undeniable, Giorgione had in Venice itself a much greater source of inspiration. Carpaccio, who would have appealed to him not only because of his similarity of expression, but because of his poetic feeling and tonal vitality.

To sum up this early formative period of Giorgione, the question may be posed whether he was not—as were other painters of his time—a self-taught artist. It is not irreverent, in fact, to call him a dilettante—quickly qualifying that word with, of genius. What is meant is that, with him, the motives behind his personality were stronger than those of his cultural milieu, though he may have been abundantly gifted in other fields, such as literature, music and perhaps even philosophy. Certainly his freedom of expression was never stifled by academicism. Grammar and rhetoric are never set above or against his poetry. This ultimately explains why his art suddenly expanded, as it were, into the fullness of his inspirational energy, achieved force, the *lontananza*, and the absolute of his representational medium—color.

Since it is usual for a young artist to be influenced by his master, it becomes of special interest to discover the point when the embryo of his own personality emerges in his work.

There is a small canvas in the Rasini Collection, in Milan, depicting *Judith* (plate 11), which the author insists upon attributing to the youthful Giorgione. Some parts of the painting definitely appear to be drawn and painted by Cima. This applies to the two women and especially to *Judith* herself. Furthermore, the general composition recalls the two frontal paintings on a chest which Berenson has attributed to Cima. The landscape, on the other hand, reminds one of Bellini. But consider the sense of fantasy, the animation of the invention, and the atmospheric control which conditions the picture's entire development! As compared to Cima's bucolic works, fresh and earthy as they are, we see here the whole spectacle moving away from us, almost out of focus, we feel that the picture's sense of life is melting away into a slow and subtle reverie, that its "story" is being diluted through the landscape into the separate episodes of these absent-minded characters: the heavy sleep of the Turk on the right, and the dialogue on the left between the other Turk and a young man in fashionable clothes. These two are definitely Giorgionesque, and the same might be said of the trees in this picture, with their elastic, vibrating trunks, and also of the plants in the copse seen on the left; this type of flora recalls the vegetation in the two small panels in the Uffizi's *Judgement of Solomon*, and *Trial of Moses* (plates 12 and 13), and also in the *Gypsy and Soldier* (plate 54). The foliage is different from the customary styles of that period, and peculiar to Giorgione. This fusion of obvious contributions by Cima and Giorgione, in a Giorgionesque atmosphere, could easily and simply be explained by the theory that Cima was Giorgione's master. It would not seem unreasonable that the lad from Castelfranco, after his arrival in Venice, chose as his teacher the elderly and reputable artist who not only had come from the mainland like himself, but was actually a native of Conegliano, a town very near Castelfranco. Furthermore, it is worth while noticing that Cima must certainly have been in contact with the Ferrara School, and this could be the explanation for Giorgione's occasional classicist attitudes.

To trace Giorgione's career and to establish the dates of his works is an extremely difficult task for a critic because of the limited knowledge we have of his life and the uncertainty surrounding the authorship of many paintings attributed to him. The very fact that his working life spanned a period of only twelve to fifteen years at the most helps to explain the disconcerting variety of opinions held by critics about Giorgione.

For this reason it becomes necessary to attempt a reconstruction of the painter's inner artistic development with respect to external cultural stimuli on the basis of the few essential elements which we can deduce from those paintings known for certain to be his own, and from the works of experts of high repute, such as L. Venturi, G. Fiocco and A. Morassi. Even so, there is the constant danger of being too subjective and arbitrary in judgement.

After his student debut consisting of the Rasini *Judith*, and after a first experience of mural decoration in which he displayed remarkable gifts of invention (the frescos in the Pelizzari house in Castelfranco, plates 1–10), Giorgione presumably studied the works of Bellini and Antonello, but above all the works of Nature. We can picture him slowly realizing the secret of his own art, becoming more and more fascinated by distance as a fundamental pictorial motive, and discovering pure color as his best means of expression.

At first, his discoveries led him only to a partial representation of distance as a true and proper phenomenon, and he reduced his scene to very small dimensions. The density of his colors insured a tonal richness which balanced the shadows and unified the scene in a comparative darkness from which some very bold and intense new harmonies emerged. While he was still experimenting with color, he gave full rein to a freedom of invention which derived its themes from life, from history and from legends. The foremost works of this period are some small panels, of which two beautiful ones are now in the Padua Museum (plates 16 and 17). In *Leda and the Swan* (plate 16), Leda's rosy flesh stands out between the two whites of the sheet and of the swan, against the green of the bushes and meadows across which flashes the purple gown of the running woman, with her sleeves of bottle-green sparkling with emeralds and amethysts. In the *Pastoral Scene* (plate 17), the amaranthus of the woman's dress contrasts with the yellow shawl around her knees, while the man wears a brick-red doublet and silvery-white hose. These quick flashes of color make the figures stand out against the dark green meadow which fades away into the blue of the sea and then into the lighter blue of the sky.

In the two Uffizi panels, the *Trial of Moses* (plate 13) and the *Judgement of Solomon* (plate 12), Giorgione showed a great independence of invention—the subject of the *Trial* was quite unusual—but somehow did not achieve the same fortunate expressions, the same perfect balance between poetic feeling and pictorial language, as in the Padua masterpieces. The Uffizi works, which still betray an excessive interest in illustration as such, bring up the problem of Giorgione's collaborators. It is a known and obvious fact that in the *Judgement of Solomon* the arid, awkward figures, and the gesture of the ruffian holding the child, are by another, a mediocre, even incompetent hand. In the *Trial of Moses*, according to some critics, Giorgione painted only the left-hand group; to Longhi, only the central figures; and the other figures could be said to recall some unknown painter of the Ferrara School (one is tempted to think of Dosso). In the landscape too some contrasts are noticeable, not so much in style as in quality.

In the author's opinion as far as the *Trial of Moses* is concerned, discrimination is difficult because even though there is a slight difference between the facial peculiarities of the central group and those of the other figures, the standard of both is very high and the styles are similar. As for the landscapes of the two panels (see plates 14 and 15), I would say that they are both equally beautiful and fascinating for their inventiveness, their sincerity, and the romantic lyricism of their inspiration.

G. Fiocco believes Giorgione's collaborator in the *Judgement of Solomon* to have been Giulio Campagnola, because the figure of Moses' mother in the *Trial* is an exact copy from one of Campagnola's frescos in Padua. Morassi, on the other hand, thinks of Giorgione's workshop companion, Catena. Some coincidences of style led the author to accept, as more probable, Fiocco's theory, even though the fact that Giorgione copied a figure from Campagnola does not necessarily prove that they worked together. On other occasions Campagnola copied Giorgione's works.

Similarly, the author would attribute to Campagnola the two panels depicting the *Story of Paris* belonging to Lord Conway and kept in Allington Castle, Maidstone (see plate 104). The small figures are exactly like those in the *Judgement of Solomon*, while the landscapes are merely void and confused commonplaces, entirely lacking in the poetic truth of the two Uffizi panels.

It is more difficult to form an opinion about the Frankfurt *Finding of Romulus and Remus* (plate 101) because of the poor condition of the panel. However, by revealing the painting's preparatory elements, it offers us a precious technical document. Both the figures and the landscape are of a higher quality than those of the *Story of Paris*, so that the work might be placed—though still with reservations—among those paintings by Giorgione in which he chose mythological subjects, sacred themes, or other episodes in order to paint fanciful landscapes around his figures rather than to place his figures in the landscapes. This genre of his was immediately and widely imitated, as shown by the above-mentioned *Story of Paris* and also by Previtali's *Four Stories of Thyrsis and Damon* (plates 102 and 103), purchased in 1937 by the National Gallery, London, as works of Giorgione. The latter certainly painted, as confirmed by

Michiel, *The Finding   Paris*, a fragment of which is in the Budapest Museum. The whole picture is known to us, thanks to a copy by David Teniers the Younger, in Florence. Of *The Finding of Paris* Michiel wrote: "It was among his first works."

Mention should be made here of a small panel in London's National Gallery, *The Adoration of the Magi*, an affectionate, almost intimate, idyll in which the characters, all of modest appearance, are scattered about the scene, contrary to the common practice of impressive choreography. It is interesting to note the resemblance between some of the characters with those on the right side of the *Trial of Moses*.

This must have been painted at the time when Da Vinci's ideas came to enrich Giorgione's experience so that he gradually developed a fuller awareness of his great powers. This period indeed must have seen Giorgione becoming more familiar with terms such as density of air and softening of contours until he found an entirely new vision into which nearness and distance could finally be unified. The *Adoration of the Magi* became, in fact, the starting point of a series of religious works such as the *Holy Family* (plate 30); the so-called *Allendale Nativity* (plate 33), in which one may observe the Leonardesque quality of the flora, and a copy of which is now in Vienna (plate 100); the Leningrad *Judith* (plate 38), and, finally, the *Castelfranco Madonna* (plate 42).

Parallel to these pictures was a series of portraits among which were the Brunswick *Self-portrait* (plate 62), described by Morassi as "one of Giorgione's most Leonardesque works", the *Portrait of a Youth* in Berlin (plate 66), and a series of idealized heads which included young shepherds with arrows, flutes or apples, a *David* (plate 64) and a *Laura* in Vienna (plate 41) dated 1506. Possibly of the same period is the *Portrait of an Old Woman* (color plate IV), perhaps Giorgione's mother; others have described her as "of a revolting realism", but she is definitely a figure of deep sadness, and her face is not devoid of affection.

So far as the two sacred subjects are concerned (plates 30 and 33), the critics are now beginning to ascribe these to Giorgione; there are, in fact, many points of contact between the London *Adoration* and the figures of Mary and Joseph in the *Allendale Nativity*, all standing out against the dark backgrounds of grottos and walls. There is no discussion whatsoever about the attribution of the Berlin *Portrait of a Youth*; though once attributed to Boccacino, the Vienna *Laura* is now widely accepted as an autograph work, thanks to the inscription on the back which tells us that in 1506 Giorgione was a colleague of Vincenzo Catena. The other idealized heads and the *Self-portrait* are more or less recorded in ancient texts, but some of them, perhaps, are copies. The authorship of the *Castelfranco Madonna* is not corroborated by documentary evidence but very few doubts can be raised about it. The probable date of its execution is *circa* 1505.

Though greatly admired, this work has been the subject of considerable criticism in the last twenty-five years. Hourticq, a brilliant scholar and a great art expert, pointed out many errors in the perspective of the painting. On the other hand Cavalcaselle, who was an able draftsman, pronounced the perspective "scientifically correct". Hourticq also criticized the use Giorgione made in this case of the theory of shadow. Others accuse the master of "timidity"; still others dislike the masking of the skyline by what they call the "trick" of that panel of red velvet, and describe the composition as "not organic".

The author would say, on the other hand, that the rigorous pyramidal scheme of the painting gives to the composition a tight central unity and purifies our vision by limiting it to the bare essentials, namely to the area where the majesty of the divine apparition dissolves in human tenderness. There is a well-defined ascent, marked by the three horizontal planes which cut through the pyramid's sides, and by the vertical areas of the throne, mounting up to the Virgin from the cold marble of the floor to the compact warmth of the red drapery, beyond which the free, open landscape surrounds the *Madonna* with an abundance of skylines.

The gentle breath of color lightly caresses this linear composition, so simply and severely geometrical, and imparts a warmth to the vast, still areas, filled only with silence and devoid of all passion. One should speak of reverence, then, rather than of timidity, on the part of the painter, who thus succeeds in passing on to the spectator an immediacy of emotion such as one finds only in true poetry. In fact, would it not really be more apt to pay tribute to Giorgione's courage in composing such a great musical work with so few notes? It does not seem out of place to call the Castelfranco panel one of the purest and most convincing of his masterpieces.

This work was probably followed by *The Three Philosophers* (plate 48), and by the *Gypsy and Soldier* (plate 54). The authorship of both paintings is acknowledged by Michiel. They are both rich with cultural implications and literary meanings, always profoundly transfigured, and both works have given rise to much speculation.

The most probable interpretation of the *Gypsy and Soldier* is by Stefanini, who connects it to the *Hypnerotomachia Poliphili*, though X-rays of the painting have revealed, under the soldier's figure, that of another bathing woman.

As far as *The Three Philosophers* is concerned—and always

28

assuming that one may give a definite meaning to these works of an essentially poetic nature—one could accept the theory of Ferriguto, who saw in it a reference to the various currents of thought prevailing at the time in Padua, interconnected to a representation of the Magi. Michiel and Berenson state that the work was finished by Sebastiano del Piombo.

These two paintings were executed approximately between 1506 and 1508. Giorgione was still immersing figures into a landscape, but now there seemed to be a new link of affection between the two components. While *The Three Philosophers* is a proof of the master's full ripening as an artist, the *Gypsy and Soldier* too—still attacked by some critics as a timid and disconnected work—shows a more expert handling of the brush, which had now become docile and entirely subservient to each subtle whim of Giorgione's fancy. This could be taken as evidence that between these two paintings and the previous ones some time had elapsed in the painter's brief career.

The years 1507–8 mark the official acknowledgement of Giorgione's prestige with the commission of a picture for the Doge's Palace in Venice (no trace remains of this work) and his employment, with other artists, to decorate with frescos the exterior of the new Fondaco dei Tedeschi, the previous building having been destroyed by fire in 1504. There are many descriptions of this work, but all that is left of it is a Venus, reduced to a few blobs of red paint. Vasari, however, who saw Giorgione's frescos on the Fondaco, wrote that he "thought only of executing fanciful figures which would show his ability. . . . Here is a man, there a woman . . . it is impossible to tell what it all means."

This, in fact, marks the beginning of Giorgione's new manner, his "grand manner", peculiar to the last two years of his life. In the author's view, the painter derived it from the experiences which he underwent while working on the Fondaco frescos and not, as Vasari might appear to suggest in his chapter on Titian, from the reciprocal influence that Giorgone and Titian had upon one another. Nor would it be acceptable that only in 1507 did Giorgione entirely change his taste and his style; in other words, that he did not acquire a new chromatic vision of the world until that year. We have already noted that Giorgione's tendency to paint in pure color was manifest from his very first efforts. Equally, Vasari's story that at the time Giorgione was congratulated for a Symbol of Justice painted by Titian on another side of the Fondaco, and as a result "would not speak to Titian again, and they were no longer friends", is now considered by many as malicious gossip emanating from Titian's idolatrous admirers. These (as stated by D. Phillips in *The Leadership of Giorgione*) "were anxious to exalt their hero at his leader's expense".

It is perfectly admissible, on the other hand, that the fresco practice which is, materially speaking, big, may have broadened Giorgione's pictorial language and thereby helped the development of his final style. Last but not least, one may assume that, to obtain from the Venice Signoria such an important commission as the Fondaco decorations, Giorgione must have previously shown that he had mastered the fresco technique.

The theory of a revolution in Giorgione's painting as opposed to the theory of his development would appear to clash also with Vasari's whole presentation of the master's life which he carefully revised in his second edition of the *Lives*. He omitted from this edition's preamble, for instance, the reference to the *Storm at Sea* (plate 120) which he had first attributed to Giorgione, but he left in it the substance of his parallel between Da Vinci and Giorgione, and particularly the words: "He liked that (Leonardo's) manner so much that he followed it as long as he lived." With regard to those last two years, we should speak of an ascent more than of a turning point, the trail of which had been already blazed by Giorgione's earlier works. Let us finally remember that Bellini, in his *San Zaccaria Altarpiece* (1505), was already Giorgionesque; in fact he was like both Giorgione and Da Vinci.

This is the period which causes the greatest controversy in the attribution of works to Giorgione, to Titian and other followers, especially to Sebastiano del Piombo. The great variety of opinions—some authoritative—proves how difficult it is to feel reasonably sure about any picture, particularly since Michiel informs us that a number of Giorgione's paintings were finished or reconditioned by Titian and Sebastiano. Hourticq has analytically compared the Louvre's *"Concert Champêtre"* (plates 72–73) with one of Titian's drawings in the Malcolm Collection (British Museum) in order to prove that Titian executed both, but his arguments are not entirely convincing. Unfortunately one cannot do more than refer each controversial work, in its more intimate and essential aspects, to one's concept of Giorgione's style, and proceed from there. Such an image, of course, should not be too rigid, but in order to distinguish between Giorgione and Titian, one should look for a line separating breadth from opulence, intensity of contrasts in color from mere chiaroscuro plasticity, and—on the psychological plane—lyricism from dramatization. There is in Giorgione an inner quality of almost virgin immaturity which is so different from Titian's exuberance. Compare, for instance, the Prado *Madonna* (plate 80) with Titian's *Gypsy Madonna* in Vienna, or the Louvre's *"Concert Champêtre"* with

31

the Pitti Palace *Concert* (plate 117), or finally the Dresden *Sleeping Venus* (plate 68) with the nude figure in Titian's *Sacred and Profane Love* in Rome.

The *Portrait of a Man*, also described as the *Terris Portrait* (plate 90), now in San Diego, was most probably painted by Giorgione during the period of which we are writing, as it bears on the back what appears to be the date 1508. The quality of the chiaroscuro recalls Da Vinci's *sfumato*, but unfortunately the picture adds little to our knowledge of Giorgione's work.

The most controversial subjects, so far as attribution is concerned, are the *Sleeping Venus* and the "*Concert Champêtre*". The attribution to Giorgione of the *Venus* was due to Morelli whose enthusiasm, since he identified the picture as the one mentioned by Michiel, is easy to understand. It was an important discovery, but now others have cast new doubts upon it and would ascribe it to Titian. The author believes that the severe innocence of the young woman's body, the musical quality of the lines, the feeling of confident repose as she sleeps alone, surrounded by silence, are typical of Giorgione. Michiel tells us of a Cupid added to the scene by Titian, but later removed, which was just as well as it certainly would have disturbed, by a beginning of action, the integrity of the silence of that solitude. The episode shows the difference in temperament between the two men.

Some would also attribute to Titian the "*Concert Champêtre*" (plates 72–73). But here, too, the connexion between the landscape and those vague, remote figures is so thin as to suggest the hand of Giorgione, perhaps stretched to the utmost of his warmth of atmosphere and generosity of form. The supreme apathy of the figures' expressions and the lack of meaning in their action appear to underline the divine and eternal freedom of poetry. Whatever Titian may have added, Giorgione conceived and executed the "*Concert Champêtre*". Both Berenson and D. Philipps are agreed that Giorgione alone is in this painting, both in spirit and in substance.

The author is equally convinced, on the other hand, that the *Concert* in the Pitti Palace (plate 117) is by Titian. The nervous hands of the player, full of tension, and his burning eyes, seem to confirm it, as indeed does the picture's whole electric atmosphere. Venturi, however, in his essay of 1954, accepts it as Giorgione's work.

Of the portraits, one might accept Longhi's attribution to Giorgione of the *Double Portrait* in Rome's Palazzo Venezia, with its thoughtful young man in the foreground (plate 89), but not the otherwise beautiful and passionate *Portrait of Antonio Broccardo* in Budapest (plate 106) which remains disturbingly enigmatic. Equally, the calm, relaxed *Knight of Malta* (plate 85) in the Uffizi was painted by Giorgione, but not the *Gattamelata Portrait* (plate 107) tense with energy and perhaps too "dry" in the contours of its round surfaces.

The author would exclude from Giorgione's authorship the *Judgement of Solomon* at Kingston Lacy (plate 114), painted by Sebastiano del Piombo, *Susannah and Daniel* in Glasgow (plate 116), which the author also believes to be by Sebastiano, and the *Sacred Conversation* in Venice (plate 115), probably by Sebastiano but also possibly by a very young Palma. Rejected, too, would be the attribution of the beautiful, but difficult to define, *The Three Ages of Man* in the Pitti Palace (plate 109).

The two heads in Rome's Borghese Gallery (plates 111 and 112) are undoubtedly magnificent, a feat of "bravura", but no more than that; even if they were not painted a century after Giorgione's death, as some would have it, the two canvases would still seem more recent, by a few decades, than the rest of the master's works. And at any rate, how can we believe that Giorgione, in the very last days of his life, should have suddenly succumbed to melodramatic theatricality? Why should he have given up his birthright of self-discipline, of intimacy, of discrimination, for such a display of loud plebeian gaudiness? Admittedly, a genius has the right to change his thoughts and his mood in the course of his career, but we do not have the right to impose such changes upon him when there are no solid grounds for such suspicions.

There are grounds, on the other hand, for attributing to Giorgione a work comparable to the *Sleeping Venus*, and which could mark the ultimate stage in the master's development, as it coincides perfectly with it and with his inspiration. This is the *Warrior with Page*, in the Spanio Collection in Venice (plate 86).

This painting's prestige is proven by the many and ancient copies of it. The one shown in this book, however, the author considers to be an original. The soft atmosphere enveloping the figures does not detract from the splendid brushwork depicting every detail of the shapes, and the subtlest shades of light and color, but always with that discretion which is so typical of Giorgione; a hint here, an allusion there, are sufficient to bring out the correct importance of each detail: the well-polished cuirasse, the scarf of finest veiling, the slits in the boy's doublet, the edges of his cap, the plumes, the strap, the hair. The figures' complexions are extremely warm, and well-harmonized: the bottle-green of the page's sleeve, the plum-colored doublet, the glowing red of his cap against the clouded gray-blue sky.

The most moving elements of this picture are perhaps to be found in the boy's podgy hands and in the loving care which he puts into the unfastening of his master's straps. The latter, as he surveys the operation with his lower lip protruding, indicates, by the disarrangement of his perspiring hair, that his helmet has just been removed. Probably this is a pause during a battle. Observe that, were he well-combed and more magnificently attired, this could be the same man portrayed in the *Knight of Malta* (plate 85). In fact, this knight, too, belongs to the Order, as shown by the cross on his scarf.

Finally, technical affinities exist between this picture and the *Portrait of a Youth* (plate 88), universally attributed to Titian, but I dare to ascribe it to Giorgione. It is hoped that a *Dead Christ* will soon be on view to the public. This painting is described on page 58, note 15.

Such, I think, was Giorgione, the ultimate Giorgione, whose works that I have recalled give us an image that no other painting would confirm. If Giorgione was the inventor of modern painting, then his teaching goes well beyond painting itself. I know that what I am about to say will make both sceptics and intellectual critics smile, but I must say it all the same, in order to try and make contact with the artist's soul and his poetry, now that we have learned to understand his language.

Undoubtedly Giorgione must have had days when he felt tired, bad-tempered, absent-minded, or just indolent. And possibly, in those moments, he may have produced indifferent works, which have been the source of much perplexity to others. But in his moments of inspiration, of that total commitment which is the artist's real morality, works were born of a beauty which will never fade, full as they were of a pure, youthful charm that sets them apart from all the others. They produce the same pleasure which we feel when, walking along a country road, the wind brings to us suddenly, a hundred yards away, the scent of the humble *Olea fragrans* from behind a garden wall.

If there was a form of painting tantamount to a catharsis, this was Giorgione's: a liberation from the weight of matter. His eyes were as clear as the morning, his affections had the innocence of spring, his dreams the limpidness of a pool of water. Let us grant Titian his midday sun, his glow and his summer: Giorgione, by following his lonely individual trial of *lontananza*, of detachment, achieved the classic serenity of the ancient Athenians.

Giorgione, the painter, taught other painters that, beyond the beautiful colors mixed upon their palettes, there is the beauty of color in a work of art. He was undoubtedly a man who knew about carnal love. By the innocence of his work he has taught us that love survives mortal flesh, and only then does it become real love.

BIOGRAPHICAL NOTES

1476–8. Birth of Giorgione. In the first edition of his *Lives of the artists* Vasari writes that Giorgione from "Castelfranco sul Trevisano was born in the year MCCCCLXX-VII". In the second edition Vasari changed this date to "1478, when Giovan Mozenigo was Doge of Venice". The biographer adds that Giorgione died of the plague in 1511 at the age of thirty-four. This date cannot be right as other reliable documents confirm that the artist died in 1510. Among these contradictions and inexactitudes it would appear that Vasari's statement in the second edition about Giorgione's birth is the correct one, for Giovanni Mocenigo, as the name is spelled today, was indeed elected Doge in 1478.

1506, JUNE 1. Giorgione shares a workshop with Catena. He paints the *Laura* in Vienna. On the back of the painting is the inscription: "On the first of June 1506 this was executed by the hands of Master Zorzi of Castelf., a colleague of Master Vizenzo Chaena at the request of Master Giacomo. . . ."

1507–8. Works for the Doge's Palace: on August 14, the payment is ordered of a sum of twenty ducats for a *Telero* in the Audience Hall; on January 24, 1508, payment is ordered of twenty-five ducats; on May 23, thirty-five lire and eighteen soldi are to be paid to the architect Giorgio Spavento for a curtain for the *Telero* in the Audience Hall. The work, which is unknown, was considered to be finished on that last date.

1508. Works for the Fondaco dei Tedeschi: on November 8, the Providers of Salt are instructed to "do justice" to "Mistro Zorzi da Castelfranco" who has stated that he was dissatisfied with the payment received for painting the Fondaco. On December 11, an Arbitration Committee is appointed, including Lazzaro Bastiani, Vittore Carpaccio and Vittore de Matio, to estimate the value of "the paintings on the front of the Fondaco dei Tedeschi, by Mistro Zorzi da Castelfrancho". The work was valued at one hundred and fifty ducats but, with the approval of "the aforementioned Mistro Zorzi", only one hundred and thirty ducats were paid to him.

1508. Painting of the so-called *Terris Portrait*, as recorded in an inscription on the back of the picture.

1510, AUTUMN. Death of Giorgione. On October 23, he had been dead only a short while; on that date Isabella d'Este, Marchioness of Mantua, wrote to the Orator Taddeo Albano, in Venice, instructing him to buy a "painting of a night" (nativity) which should have been among Giorgione's belongings. Albano replied on November 7, that Giorgione "died several days ago of the plague". The plague is recalled also in the diary of Marin Sanudo. It was a particularly virulent one, especially between September 12 and 27. This would confirm Vasari's version of Giorgione's death, though the biographer mistook the year in which it took place. As regards the "painting of a night" mentioned by Isabella, Albano replied that such a picture did not appear among the master's belongings, but added that "Taddeo Contarino owns one, and Vittorio Beccari a better one". However, Albano goes on to say: "neither picture can be bought at any price, because they commissioned them for their own enjoyment".

GIORGIONE'S PAINTINGS

Plate 1

MEDALLION. *Fragment of a fresco, detached from those in the Pellizzari house, shown in the following plates. Castelfranco, Casa Rostirolla.*

Plates 2-6

FRESCOS *in a large room of the Pellizzari house in Castelfranco. Strip* (*On the north-west wall 156·8 × 75·5, south-east wall 158·3 × 63**). Strip of yellow tones, with white lights and black shadows, the whole in chiaroscuro: instruments pertaining to the various sciences, medallions, cameos and latin mottos. Cavalcaselle, and later Borenius, were the first to give these frescos serious consideration. Richter, Morassi and Fiocco ascribe them to Giorgione, helped perhaps by some assistant. Such decorations are fairly traditional on the Venetian mainland, both without and within the houses, and they are often entrusted to eminent artists. It is not surprising, therefore, that Giorgione should have had a hand in these frescos, especially as they seem to reveal something of his genius for invention and originality. He was probably very young at the time of their execution, though they may also be dated from a time nearer the painting of the *Castelfranco Madonna* (plate 42). (See also plates 7-10.)

Plates 7-10

FRESCOS *in the Pellizzari house as described above.* Details of medallions,

geographical and astronomical drawings and instruments of the military, musical and representational arts.

Plate 11

JUDITH. *Canvas, 50 × 60. Milan, Rasini Collection.* I believe it to be one of Giorgione's early works. (See page 21.)

Plate 12

JUDGEMENT OF SOLOMON. *Panel, 89 × 12. Florence, Uffizi Gallery.* In 1692, this panel and the next one (*Trial of Moses*) were part of the Grand Duke of Tuscany's collection at Poggio Imperiale. They were also unsigned. In 1793 they were transferred to the Uffizi as works of Giovanni Bellini. Cavalcaselle's attribution of them to Giorgione and his assistants was generally accepted. As to the identity of the assistants, Fiocco suggests Giulio Campagnola for the figures in the *Judgement of Solomon*, and the landscape of the *Trial of Moses*; Morassi thinks Vincenzo Catena contributed to the *Judgement*; Longhi attributes to an unknown artist of the Ferrara School the lateral figures of the *Trial*. This work, in the author's opinion, was carried out almost entirely by Giorgione, whereas in the *Judgement* the artist was responsible for the composition and landscape, and probably left the figures to Campagnola. Whilst the theme of the *Judgement of Solomon* was a fairly common one, the subject of the *Trial of Moses* was

* All dimensions are given in centimeters.

39

extremely unusual, and was inspired by the Talmud in which it is written that the child Moses, confronted with the choice between a platter laden with jewels and a red hot brazier, chose the latter. (See also plate 14.)

Plate 13

TRIAL OF MOSES. *Panel, 89 × 12. Florence, Uffizi Gallery.* See comment on plate 12. (See also plate 15.)

Plate 14

JUDGEMENT OF SOLOMON. *Florence, Uffizi Gallery.* Detail of landscape.

Plate 15

TRIAL OF MOSES. *Florence, Uffizi Gallery.* Detail of landscape.

Plate 16

LEDA AND THE SWAN. *Small panel, 12 × 19. Padua, Museo Civico.* This panel should be associated with three others shown in plates 17, 18 and 19 (and perhaps with a fifth one kept in the Suardo Collection at Bergamo). The almost perfect coincidence of these panels' dimensions, and the fact that they are all more or less similar in style, suggests the possibility that they may have graced a single piece of furniture, perhaps a small jewel coffer. Indeed they may have come from the house of the Falier family at Asolo and, if it were so, the attribution to Giorgione would be even further corroborated. This *Leda and the Swan*, together with the *Pastoral Scene* (plate 17), comes from the Emo Capodilista Collection. The directors of the Museo Civico attributed them (with some reservations) to Giorgione, but Cook, Lord Conway, Fiocco and Morassi were definite in their attribution;

Justi and Venturi ascribe it to an imitator, others to Campagnola.

Plate 17

PASTORAL SCENE. *Small panel, 12 × 19. Padua, Museo Civico.* See under plate 16. Observe how the arrangement of this scene foreshadows, in terms of theme, that of the *Gypsy and Soldier*.

Plate 18

ALLEGORY OF TIME. *Small panel, 12 × 19. Washington, Phillips Collection.* See what has been written for plate 16. This tablet, attributed by B. Berenson to a "Giorgionesque furniture painter", came originally from the Pulszky Collection in Budapest which consists mainly of pictures from the Veneto; in 1937 it was moved to the St Luke Gallery in Vienna. Later still it was acquired by the Thyssen Collection, Lugano. Many critics agree that it was painted by the same hand as the two Padua tablets (plates 16 and 17).

Plate 19

LANDSCAPE WITH NYMPH AND CUPID. *Small panel, 11 × 20. Washington, National Gallery of Art, Kress Collection.* See under plate 16. The panel comes from the Collection of Count Falier at Castelle d'Asolo and was bought by the Kress Foundation in 1939. Morassi considers the painter to have been Previtali. Others, like de Batz, find in it elements common to the three previous tablets (plates 16, 17 and 18). Berenson dismisses it as, again, the work of "a Giorgionesque furniture painter".

Plate 20

ALLEGORY OF CHASTITY. *Canvas, 28 × 39. Amsterdam, Lanz Collection.* The painting comes from the

Kaufmann Collection where it was attributed to Giorgione, with the endorsement of Bode and Richter. Morassi and Fiocco accept this with reservations. Berenson, Monneret and Justi believe it to be by a Giorgionesque painter. Frizzoni believes it to be a copy.

Plate 21

AENEAS AND ANCHISES. *Canvas, 71 × 90. London, private collection.* This painting comes from the Dona' delle Rose Collection in Venice, acquired in turn from the Villa Garzoni at Ponte Casale in 1933. The attribution to Giorgione is opposed by Lorenzetti who ascribes the canvas to Campagnola. Richter and Morassi reserve their judgement. Fiocco thought at first of Campagnola, then revised his opinion and accepted Giorgione's authorship. G. Sangiorgi (*Illustrated London News*) believes this picture to be the one listed by Michiel, who had seen, in Taddeo Contarini's house, "a large oil painting of Hades, with Aeneas and Anchises". Longhi is definitely in favor of Giorgione. The canvas was not accepted as a work of the Castelfranco master at the time of its export. It had been repainted and restored twice and may have been altered. However, as far as one can tell from photographs, the scenic invention, the structure, the contrast in the landscape between light and shadow—so reminiscent of the *Allendale Nativity* (plate 33) and of *The Three Philosophers* (plate 48)— are so very Giorgionesque, and of such a high quality as to make Longhi's view completely acceptable.

Plate 22a

PARIS ON MOUNT IDA. *Panel, 38 × 56.5. Princeton, University Art Museum, the property of Frank Jewett Mather, Jr.* Attributed to Giorgione by Professor Mather, Sr., with the endorsement of Lord Conway, Richter, de Batz and Morassi. Fiocco believes it to be the work of an imitator.

Plate 22b

COUNTRY LANDSCAPE. *Panel, 46 × 44. Northampton, Castle Ashby.* Lord Conway and Fiocco attribute it to Giorgione. Berenson disagrees.

Plate 23

THE FINDING OF PARIS. *Canvas, 91 × 63. Budapest Museum.* This is only a fragment of a larger picture —some five feet wide—recalled by Michiel in Taddeo Contarini's house, "the canvas of a landscape with the birth of Paris, and two shepherds standing by". The scene was engraved by Van Kessel in *Theatrum pictorium* in 1659, and copied by Teniers the Younger (see plate 96b). This fragment, showing the two shepherds and a portion of the child's head, is considered an original by Morelli, Justi and others, and with reservations by Morassi. Fiocco is not alone in describing it as a copy. The many repaintings make it very difficult to express an opinion.

Plate 24

MADONNA READING. *Panel, 75.5 × 61. Oxford, Ashmolean Museum.* Detail. Known also as the *Tallard Madonna*, this was part of the Duke of Tallard's Collection in 1756, and was sold as a Cariani at Christies on May 13, 1949, when it was bought by the Ashmolean Museum and acknowledged as a Giorgione by K. T. Parker. The critics were almost unanimous in accepting this attribution, with the exception of

Berenson. Morassi thinks it a late work by the master, datable about 1507-8. The whole picture can be seen in the next plate (color plate I).

Plate 25

ADORATION OF THE MAGI. *Predella panel, 30 × 81. London, National Gallery.* In 1882 this panel was part of the Miles Collection, at Leigh Court, as a work by Giovanni Bellini. It has been in the National Gallery since 1884. Cavalcaselle, Berenson, Justi, Fiocco and Morassi claim that it was painted by Giorgione; A. Venturi sees it as the work of an anonymous Giorgionesque painter; Morelli attributes it to Catena and so does L. Venturi; Richter is doubtful and tends to favor Giorgione but with the participation of Bellini's workshop. This is obviously an early work, closely connected with the Washington *Holy Family* (plate 30). It contains a few odd facial features recalling the *Trial of Moses* (plate 13). The author would connect it with the *Madonna Reading* (color plate I) and with the *Allendale Nativity* reproduced in plates 33-37. (See also plates 26-29.)

Plate 26

ADORATION OF THE MAGI. *London, National Gallery.* Detail of the Virgin and Child.

Plate 27

ADORATION OF THE MAGI. *London, National Gallery.* Detail of St Joseph.

Plate 28

ADORATION OF THE MAGI. *London, National Gallery.* Detail of the Magi.

Plate 29

ADORATION OF THE MAGI. *London, National Gallery.* Detail of two grooms.

Plate 30

HOLY FAMILY. *Panel, 21 × 25. Washington, National Gallery of Art, Kress Collection.* Bought from an antiquarian in 1887 by Henry Willet, it went later to the Benson Collection, London (hence the title of the *Benson Holy Family*); when this collection was dispersed it was acquired by Lord Duveen, who later passed it on to the Kress Collection. It is acknowledged as a Giorgione by H. Cook, Justi, Suida, Berenson, Richter, Morassi and Fiocco. Berenson and L. Venturi had at first thought it a Catena. (See also plates 31 and 32.)

Plate 31

HOLY FAMILY. *Washington, National Gallery of Art.* Detail of central group.

Plate 32

HOLY FAMILY. *Washington, National Gallery of Art.* Detail of landscape in the right-hand background.

Color Plate I

MADONNA READING. *Oxford, Ashmolean Museum.* (See plate 24.)

Plate 33

THE ALLENDALE NATIVITY. *Panel, 91 × 111. Washington, National Gallery of Art, Kress Collection.* Also known as the *Beaumont Adoration.* The Gallery's catalogue states that this may possibly be one of the *Nights* mentioned in the correspondence between Isabella d'Este and her buyer, Taddeo Albano. Morassi accepts this and specifies that in his opinion the painting is the one seen by Albano in Vittorio Beccaro's house. Morassi, however, also admits, though doubtfully, that this painting may be the "creche" evaluated by Paris Bordone in 1563 in the house of Giovanni Grimani, or even a painting which belonged to King James III of England, as stated in the Bathoe Catalogue of 1785. The painting's history can be positively traced from 1841, when Cardinal Fesch's collection was auctioned; it then passed to the Claudio Terral and later to the T. Wentworth Beaumont Collection (1847); Lord Allendale inherited it, and from him, in 1939, through the Duveen brothers, it became the property of the Kress Collection. A drawing at Windsor Castle, mentioned by Cavalcaselle and Dreyfus, is thought by Hadeln, Justi and Parker to be an autograph, whilst Popham and Morassi call it a "derivation".

The Washington panel is traditionally attributed to Giorgione by Cavalcaselle, Cook, Justi, Phillips, Morassi, Fiocco, Longhi and others. Berenson now accepts the attribution but believes the painting to have been completed by Titian. L. Venturi also has now revised his opinion and accepts it as a Giorgione. In Roger Fry's opinion the painter was Cariani; Holmes believes it to be by Bonifazio. The American Gallery's catalogue, and the greater part of the experts who acknowledge the canvas as a Giorgione, consider it an early work dating from about 1500–5. Morassi, however, believes that the master painted it later. (See also plates 34–37, and plate 100a.)

Plate 34

THE ALLENDALE NATIVITY. *Washington, National Gallery of Art*. Detail of St Joseph.

Plate 35

THE ALLENDALE NATIVITY. *Washington, National Gallery of Art*. Detail of the Virgin.

Plate 36

THE ALLENDALE NATIVITY. *Washington, National Gallery of Art*. Detail of the shepherds.

Plate 37

THE ALLENDALE NATIVITY. *Washington, National Gallery of Art*. Detail of the landscape in the left-hand background.

Plate 38

JUDITH. *Panel transferred to canvas in 1838. Leningrad, Hermitage Museum*. The picture's measurements were reduced, between 1755 and 1770, to 144 × 65; about 13 cm. were cut from each side. The panel was taken from Italy to France towards the end of 1600, and passed from one collection to the other (Bertin, Pierre Crozat in 1729, Louis Francois Crozat, Baron of Thiers, in 1740); while in the Baron's possession it was made the subject of an engraving, as a Raphael, by Toinette Larcher (*Recueil d'estampes . . .*, Paris, 1729–42) and listed in its original dimensions in 1755; it was seen and cut down to its present measurements by Saint-Aubin in 1770. In 1772 Catherine II of Russia bought it, together with the whole Crozat Collection, for the Hermitage Museum. Following Larcher's engraving, the panel continued to be ascribed to Raphael until, in 1864, Waagen suggested to Morelli, who still remained uncertain, Giorgione. This is now almost universally accepted. (See also plate 39.)

43

Plate 39

JUDITH. *Leningrad, Hermitage Museum*. Detail of Judith's face.

Plate 40

PORTRAIT OF A LADY. *Canvas, 31·7 × 24·1. New York, Duveen Brothers*. Formerly the property of Prince Lichnowsky at Kuchelna (Czechoslovakia), and later of Lord Melchett at Romsey, Hampshire. The attribution to Giorgione is accepted by Berenson, Gronau, Richter, Tietze, Richardson and de Batz. The resemblance to *Laura* (see plate 41) leads the author to share this view.

Plate 41

PORTRAIT OF LAURA. *Canvas attached to panel, 41 × 33·6. Vienna, Kunsthistorisches Museum*. Formerly in the Gallery of Archduke Leopold Wilhelm in Brussels, as shown in an inventory of 1659. Later in Vienna as part of the Imperial Collections. The painting has been attributed alternatively to Bassano, to Palma's school, to Romanino (by Engerth in 1883), and to Boccaccino by A. Venturi. In 1908 Justi, on the basis of the reading by Dollmayr of an inscription on the back of the picture, attributed it with some hesitation to Giorgione. Later he was supported almost unanimously by Longhi, Hourticq, Wilde, Hermanin, Fiocco, Morassi and Berenson. Only Richter remains doubtful.

Plate 42

MADONNA WITH SS FRANCIS AND LIBERALE. *Panel, 200 × 152. Castelfranco, Church of San Liberale*. This famous altarpiece, many times arbitrarily restored, was retouched once again in 1938 by Mauro Pellicioli, who also restored Da Vinci's *Last Supper*. Pellicioli con-

solidated the colors, but conscientiously returned to their original state all the parts which had been altered by his predecessors. For some critics, including Hourticq, the knight at left (plate 46) is St George, but there really seems to be no doubt whatsoever that it is St Liberale. The attribution to Giorgione was first made by Ridolfi who visited Castelfranco in 1640 and talked to the locals. He did not, however, state his opinion until 1684. Since then no one has disputed the authorship, though the date of execution is still a subject of discussion. Gronau and Richter, knowing that the altarpiece was intended for the Costanzo family chapel, believed that it was painted before 1504, the year of young Matteo Costanzo's death. More reasonably, others claim that the work was executed immediately after that date, by order of Matteo's father, the Condottieri Tuzio Costanzo, in memory of his son.

While the painting is generally considered one of the world's great masterpieces, Hourticq is rather critical of it and calls it "this Madone stylithe". Longhi too finds it far from perfect, pointing out here and there signs of uncertainty, of timidity, even of awkwardness. In a recent essay, however, L. Venturi proclaims once again the altarpiece's great merits.

Plate 43

MADONNA WITH SS FRANCIS AND LIBERALE. *Castelfranco, Church of San Liberale*. Detail of the Virgin and Child.

Plate 44

MADONNA WITH SS FRANCIS AND LIBERALE. *Castelfranco, Church of San Liberale*. Detail of the left-hand landscape.

Plate 45

MADONNA WITH SS FRANCIS AND LIBERALE. *Castelfranco, Church of San Liberale*. Detail of the right-hand landscape.

Plate 46

MADONNA WITH SS FRANCIS AND LIBERALE. *Castelfranco, Church of San Liberale*. Detail of St Liberale.

Plate 47

MAN IN ARMOR. *Panel, 39 × 27. London, National Gallery*. Study for the St Liberale in the Castelfranco altarpiece. On the panel is an ancient inscription with the name Giorgione. This was formerly believed to be a portrait of Gaston de Foix, possibly the same de Foix of Lord Bessborough's Collection and of the Smith Collection, both attributed to Giorgione. The painting is certainly identifiable with the Smith knight shown in 1816 and transferred in 1820 to the Rogers Collection. It was donated to the National Gallery in 1855. First attributed to Giorgione by Cavalcaselle and now by Morassi. Fiocco calls it a derivation.

Plate 48

THE THREE PHILOSOPHERS. *Canvas, 121 × 141·5. Vienna, Kunsthistorisches Museum*. This canvas, which has been cut down, especially on the left-hand side, is one of the very few paintings definitely by Giorgione. It was, in fact, minutely described by Michiel, who had seen it in 1525 in Taddeo Contarini's house. In 1659 it was quoted in the inventory of Archduke Leopold Wilhelm's Gallery; a year later it was engraved by Teniers; it later went to the Austrian Imperial Collections. Roentgen rays have revealed some departures from the original plans,

especially in the head-dress of the old philosopher on the right, who at first wore a diadem, or a fan-like crest. Many interpretations have been offered of this theme: Mechel, in his Catalogue of 1783, speaks of the "Three Wise Men", a title which has been taken up again, in modern times, by Wilde, Wisler and others; Wickhoff, in 1895, saw in the subject Evander and Pallas showing Aeneas the site of the future Capitol; Ferriguto, in 1933, suggested that each of the three figures symbolized the philosophical trends of Giorgione's days: the old man is the Aristotelian school, the figure in the turban is Averroism, while the seated youth represents the new naturalistic science then fashionable in Padua. The fact that the painting was finished by Sebastiano del Piombo, as Michiel himself tells us, does not necessarily mean that Giorgione painted it just before his death. It could have been executed some years before and left unfinished. (See also color plate II and plates 49–53.)

Color Plate II

THE THREE PHILOSOPHERS. *Vienna, Kunsthistorisches Museum*. Detail of the three figures.

Plate 49

THE THREE PHILOSOPHERS. *Vienna, Kunsthistorisches Museum*. Detail of trees and landscape.

Plate 50

THE THREE PHILOSOPHERS. *Vienna, Kunsthistorisches Museum*. Detail of central landscape.

Plate 51

THE THREE PHILOSOPHERS. *Vienna, Kunsthistorisches Museum*. Detail of the young philosopher.

Plate 52

THE THREE PHILOSOPHERS. *Vienna, Kunsthistorisches Museum.* Detail of the "Eastern" philosopher.

Plate 53

THE THREE PHILOSOPHERS. *Vienna, Kunsthistorisches Museum.* Detail of the old philosopher.

Plate 54

GYPSY AND SOLDIER. *Canvas, 78 × 72. Venice, Gallerie dell' Accademia.* Also recorded by Michiel who had seen it in 1530 in the house of Gabriele Vendramin. The canvas was still there in 1569 as indicated in an inventory of that year. In 1856, under the title of *Mercury and Isis,* it appeared in the Manfrin Gallery; Prince Giovanelli bought it in 1875, and since 1932 it has hung in the Venice Accademia. X-rays have revealed, under the soldier's figure, an earlier outline of a bathing woman (plate 57). Among the many and partly extravagant explanations of the theme, which must have appeared obscure to Giorgione's contemporaries (see Michiel), Stefanini's theory is perhaps most acceptable: he believes the canvas to have been inspired by the *Hypnerotomachia Poliphili.* There is disagreement about the date of execution. Cook thinks the canvas was painted before 1500; Conti and Borenius claim that it preceded the Castelfranco altarpiece; the majority of the others believe it to have been painted later. (See also color plate III and plates 55–60.)

Plate 55

GYPSY AND SOLDIER. *Venice, Gallerie dell' Accademia.* Detail of the woman and child.

Plate 56

GYPSY AND SOLDIER. *Venice, Gallerie dell' Accademia.* Detail of the soldier.

Color Plate III

GYPSY AND SOLDIER. *Venice, Gallerie dell' Accademia.* Detail of background, with landscape and sky.

Plate 57

GYPSY AND SOLDIER. *Venice, Gallerie dell' Accademia.* X-ray of the lower left-hand quarter showing the original figure of the bathing woman, later replaced by the soldier.

Plate 58

GYPSY AND SOLDIER. *Venice, Gallerie dell' Accademia.* Detail of soldier's head.

Plate 59

GYPSY AND SOLDIER. *Venice, Gallerie dell' Accademia.* Detail of woman's head.

Plate 60

GYPSY AND SOLDIER. *Venice, Gallerie dell' Accademia.* Detail of landscape.

Plate 61

PORTRAIT OF AN OLD WOMAN. *Venice, Gallerie dell' Accademia.* Detail of head.

Plate 62

SELF-PORTRAIT. *Canvas, 52 × 43. Brunswick, Herzog Anton Ulrich Museum.* This could be the same self-portrait seen by Vasari in the house of Grimani, Patriarch of Aquileia and from which he sketched the portrait of Giorgione shown in his biography. Hollar made an engraving of the canvas in 1650, when it was part of the van Verle Collection in Antwerp; in 1737 it was acquired by the Duke of Brunswick and recorded in a 1776 inventory as a self-portrait of Raphael; later it was described as by Dosso Dossi. The picture must have been cut down after 1650. Attributed to Giorgione by Justi, and then by Wickhoff, Hermanin, Richter, Fiocco and Morassi. For L. Venturi and others it is a copy; for Berenson a "version of Giorgione's self-portrait as David" by the elder Palma.

Plate 63

YOUTH HOLDING ARROW. *Panel, 48 × 42. Vienna, Kunsthistorisches Museum.* In 1663 this painting could be seen as an Andrea del Sarto, in Ambras Castle at Innsbruck where it had arrived from Archduke Sigismund's Collection; from 1773 it was part of the Vienna Imperial Collections; ten years later it was listed as a Schedone in Mechel's Catalogue; in 1837 Kraft's Catalogue described it as "Correggio's School". Reasonably, Ludwig identified it with the painting seen by Michiel in Giovanni Ram's house in 1531, and in the home of Antonio Pasqualino a year later. Ram had kept a copy of it which he still believed to be an original. This proves that, even shortly after Giorgione's death there was some uncertainty about this panel, and helps to explain the diverse opinions about it. The Vienna panel is believed to be the original one by Ludwig, Wickhoff, Fiocco, Morassi and Berenson; Gronau and L. Venturi see it as a copy; Mundler and Waagen ascribe it to Bernardino Gatti; Buschbeck to Lotto; Richter and Wilde are doubtful. The fine quality of the picture leads the author to accept it as the work of Giorgione.

Plate 64

DAVID WITH HEAD OF GOLIATH. *Panel, 65 × 74.5. Vienna, Kunsthistorisches Museum.* Formerly part of Archduke Leopold Wilhelm's Collection and engraved in 1660 by Teniers. Attributed by Wilde to an imitator, and by Morassi to Giorgione, although doubtfully, owing to the poor condition of the painting. The panel should find a place among the group of pictures previously discussed, which must also have included the original *Page*, of which plate 98 reproduces only a copy. This David cannot be identified with the *Self-portrait* (plate 62), because of the obvious youth of the figure.

Color Plate IV

PORTRAIT OF AN OLD WOMAN. *Canvas, 69 × 60. Venice, Gallerie dell' Accademia.* As the Vendramin coat of arms appears on the ancient frame, it is reasonable to identify this canvas with the one recorded in that family's inventory of 1569, "the portrait of Giorgione's mother, in the master's own hand, provided by him and adorned with the Vendramin heraldic arms". Later the painting passed to the Manfrin Gallery. It was first attributed to Giorgione by A. Della Rovere in 1903; Monneret, Berenson, Suida, Fiocco and Morassi are among the many who agree. Dates from about the same time as the *Gypsy and Soldier*.

Plate 65

PORTRAIT OF SHEPHERD WITH PIPE. *Canvas, 61 × 51. Hampton Court, Royal Gallery.* Acquired by King Charles I as a Giorgione, it was transferred in 1649 to the de Critz Collection, and in 1688 to King James II's Collection. In 1714 the canvas became part of Queen Anne's Collection and from that time onwards it has remained the property of the British Royal Family. The majority of modern critics agree with Morelli's original attribution to Giorgione. This is certainly true of Wickhoff, Monneret, Gronau, Berenson, Suida; Fiocco, Richter and Morassi reserve their judgement; Cook and L. Venturi ascribe the canvas to Torbido. Rather than a copy or an imitation, the author believes it to be an original variation of the *Youth holding arrow* (plate 63).

Plate 66

PORTRAIT OF A YOUTH. *Canvas, 58 × 46. Berlin, Kaiser Friedrich Museum.* Originally bought in 1884 from the Giustiniani Collection in Padua by Jean Paul Richter who in 1891 sold it to the Berlin Museum. Wickhoff attributes it to Sebastiano del Piombo, but all the others agree that it is by Giorgione. The two letters V.V. on the parapet have yet to be explained; they were probably the initials of the unknown young man. (See also plate 67.)

Plate 67

PORTRAIT OF A YOUTH. *Berlin, Kaiser Friedrich Museum.* Detail of head.

Plate 68

SLEEPING VENUS. *Canvas (transferred from the original in 1843), 108·5 × 175. Dresden, Gemäldegalerie.* Bought, in 1697, on behalf of King Augustus of Saxony by C. le Roy, a merchant. It appeared in a catalogue of 1707 as a Giorgione, but from 1722 onward it was listed as a Titian. Cleaning operations carried out in 1843 brought to light a Cupid which had been previously covered with paint. Owing to the poor condition of this detail, it was decided to cover it again. In 1880 Morelli identified this Venus with the one seen by Michiel in the home of Gerolamo Marcello. In the painting mentioned by Michiel the landscape and the Cupid had been finished by Titian. The experts accepted unanimously Morelli's attribution until, in 1919, Hourticq reduced his acknowledgement of Giorgione's direct participation to the face alone, and in 1930 pronounced himself entirely in favor of Titian. This radically negative position appealed also to Suida, who sought further evidence: (1) a document published by Fogolari about a Giorgione picture seen in the Marcello house in 1730, that is, when the *Sleeping Venus* was already in Dresden (this does not prove that the Giorgione mentioned in the document was the *Venus*); (2) some lines by the poet Boschini alluding to a different position of Venus, but which may equally apply to the Dresden painting. Morassi sides entirely with Hourticq and Suida, though he accepts the spirit of the painting as Giorgionesque, and admits that it is thanks to Giorgione that "such a pure and classical beauty has matured in Titian's art". In his opinion Titian painted this canvas at the time of his *Sacred and Profane Love.*

But, in more recent literature, critics such as Berenson, Fiocco, Longhi, L. Venturi and Gamba favor Giorgione. (See also plates 69, 70 and 71.)

Plate 69

SLEEPING VENUS. *Dresden, Gemäldegalerie.* Detail of Venus.

Plate 70

SLEEPING VENUS. *Dresden, Gemäldegalerie.* Detail of drapery.

Plate 71

SLEEPING VENUS. *Dresden, Gemälde-galerie*. Detail of the head.

Plate 72–73

"CONCERT CHAMPÊTRE". *Canvas, 110 × 138. Paris, Louvre*. Up to 1627 this picture was part of the Duke of Mantua's collection and perhaps, as Justi wrote, it may have belonged to Isabella d'Este. Later it became the property of King Charles I of England, then of the banker Jabach who sold it to Louis XIV of France. Its traditional attribution to Giorgione was contested first by Waagen, who saw it as the work of Palma the Elder, then by Lafenestre and Springer, who suggested Titian, and later still especially by Cavalcaselle, who ascribed it to an imitator of Sebastiano del Piombo. Morelli fought back for Giorgione, with the support of A. and L. Venturi, Berenson, Justi, a converted Gronau, Cook, Richter and Fiocco; but Hourticq, reinforced by Suida and Morassi, insists upon Titian who, in his opinion, began this work immediately after the Padua frescos (1511–12) but did not finish it until after 1530.

Hourticq went so far as to identify this picture with a painting of nudes which Albano, in his letters to Isabella d'Este, stated had been commissioned from Titian. However, the date of 1530 would seem to be too late. Morassi thinks that the *"Concert Champêtre"* was born in the same creative climate as the *Sleeping Venus*, perhaps a few years before. The attribution to Titian is accepted by Longhi. For the majority of critics who ascribe it to Giorgione this picture was painted after the *Sleeping Venus* and constitutes one of the last and most mature achievements of Giorgione. (See also plates 74–79.)

Plate 74

"CONCERT CHAMPÊTRE". *Paris, Louvre*. Detail of the woman on the left (upper part).

Plate 75

"CONCERT CHAMPÊTRE". *Paris, Louvre*. Detail of the woman on the right and of the man in the center.

Plate 76

"CONCERT CHAMPÊTRE". *Paris, Louvre*. Detail of the woman on the left (lower part).

Plate 77

"CONCERT CHAMPÊTRE". *Paris, Louvre*. Detail of the right-hand background: shepherd and flock.

Plate 78

"CONCERT CHAMPÊTRE". *Paris, Louvre*. Detail of the lute player.

Plate 79

"CONCERT CHAMPÊTRE". *Paris, Louvre*. Detail of the central background landscape.

Plate 80

MADONNA WITH SS ANTHONY OF PADUA AND ROCH. *Canvas, 92 × 133. Madrid, Prado Museum*. In or about 1650 this canvas was offered to Philip IV of Spain by the Viceroy of Naples, the Duke of Medina. Velazquez attributed it to Pordenone, Cavalcaselle to Francesco Vecellio, Schmidt to Titian. This last theory is obviously supported by those critics who believe that Titian painted the *Sleeping Venus* (see under plate 68) with the exception of L. Venturi. Morelli and his followers, and now also Gamba, are in favor of Giorgione. (See also plate 81.)

Plate 81

MADONNA WITH SS ANTHONY OF PADUA AND ROCH. *Madrid, Prado Museum.* Detail of the central group and St Roch.

Plate 82

CHRIST CARRYING THE CROSS. *Panel, 50 × 39. Boston (Mass.), Gardner Museum.* This panel comes from the Loschi Dal Verme Collection in Vicenza. It is generally attributed to Giorgione. Berenson qualifies: Giorgione after Giovanni Bellini, an early work; Morassi identifies it with Bellini's school, with which there certainly are similarities. A number of copies of this painting are in existence.

Plate 83

CHRIST WITH CROSS AND OTHER FIGURES. *Canvas, 70 × 100. Venice, Church of San Rocco.* The painting has been in San Rocco since it was painted. Michiel recalls, in 1552, in Antonio Pasqualino's house, a *Head of St James* by Giorgione or a pupil, taken from the *Christ of San Rocho.* It would seem reasonable, therefore, to argue that the figure of Christ was also by Giorgione—to whom Vasari attributes it in both editions of his *Lives.* But then Vasari also attributes it to Titian (in his biography of that artist), adding that "Many have thought this to be a work by Giorgione." Venturi explains the mistake by recalling that in San Rocco there is also an *Ecce homo* by Titian. To sum up, we are faced here with differences of opinion the weight of which is not easy to evaluate, for though one tends, as a rule, to accept Michiel's testimony against all others, it may well be that Vasari, in his *Life of Titian,* intended to correct himself on the basis of direct information.

Ridolfi, Boschini, and Sansovino accept the Titian authorship on the strength of Vasari's statement. The work being damaged, it is almost impossible to reach a conclusion, but the contained drama of the scene and the discipline of the attitudes would appear to indicate Giorgione as the painter. Hourticq's comparison of the head of this Christ with the Christ of the *Tribute-money* formerly in Dresden is not convincing. Cavalcaselle favors Giorgione, and so do Berenson and L. Venturi; Hourticq, Suida, Morassi and Pallucchini favor Titian. (See also plate 84.)

Plate 84

CHRIST WITH CROSS AND OTHER FIGURES. *Venice, Church of San Rocco.* Detail of the head of Christ.

Plate 85

KNIGHT OF MALTA. *Canvas, 80 × 64. Florence, Uffizi Gallery.* Formerly part of Paolo del Sera's Collection, from which, in 1654, it passed to the Medici family. Originally ascribed to Titian. Cavalcaselle attributes it to a Giorgionesque painter, Hourticq, Suida and Morassi to Titian. The majority of modern critics accept it as a Giorgione.

Plate 86

WARRIOR WITH PAGE. *Canvas, 70 × 86·5. Venice, Spanio Collection. From the Van Axel Palace Collections; previously the property of Sebastiano Barozzi.* This could be the original of a composition which was copied many times, and ought to be considered, in the author's view, one of the last and most mature works by Giorgione. This opinion is shared by Fiocco and Pallucchini, but others do not agree. Cavalcaselle, in 1871, recalled five different facsimiles of this composition, though in smaller dimensions and without the knight's helmet on the window-sill: (1) in the storage rooms of the Vienna Kunsthistorisches Museum; (2) in the Alfieri di Sostegno home in Turin; (3) in the Carlisle Collection in Naworth Castle, from the Orleans Collections; (4) in Stuttgart's Gallery; (5) a copy signed by G. Pencz in Berlin's Redern Collection. The Naworth Castle replica (now in the Howard Collection in Howard Castle), which could be an original, was reproduced by Richter; the Stuttgart copy, thought by Cavalcaselle to be a more recent copy, was found, when X-rayed, to be superimposed on a *Pieta*, dating from the first half of the sixteenth century, and was therefore eliminated; the Pencz facsimile went later to the Kaufmann Collection.

Plate 87

WARRIOR WITH PAGE. *Venice, Spanio Collection*. Detail of page.

Plate 88

PORTRAIT OF A YOUTH. *Canvas, 80·6 × 69·5. New York, Frick Collection*. Commonly attributed to Titian. Morassi claims that the similarity of style between this picture and the "*Concert Champêtre*" makes it obvious that the same artist painted both works. This is true, and the author would link with these two paintings the *Warrior with Page* (plate 86). But if one attributes to Giorgione, the "*Concert Champêtre*" and the *Warrior with Page*, then one cannot but attribute to him this portrait too, which the author consider his masterpiece in the particular field of portrait-painting.

Plate 89

DOUBLE PORTRAIT. *Canvas, 80 × 67·5. Rome, Palazzo Venezia Gallery*. Ravaglia believes the two young men to be the musicians, Verdelot and Obreth. This painting has been attributed by some to Sebastiano del Piombo. Pallucchini disagrees. Fiocco sees it as a Mancini. The attribution to Giorgione is due to Longhi, and it seems acceptable if one compares this canvas with the *Portrait of a Man* (plate 90).

Plate 90

PORTRAIT OF A MAN. *Panel, 30 × 26. San Diego, California, Fine Arts Society*. Formerly in the Currov and Terris Collections and therefore also known as the *Terris Portrait*. It bears, on the back, an ancient inscription with a date which could be read as 1508. Richter was the first to publish this canvas as a Giorgione, and Gronau, Hadeln, Suida, Fiocco Morassi and L. Venturi agree. (See also plate 91.)

Plate 91

PORTRAIT OF A MAN. *San Diego, Fine Arts Society*. Detail of the face.

Plate 92

VIEW OF CASTELFRANCO. *Red chalk on paper, 20 × 29. Rotterdam, Boymans Museum*. Until 1707 in the Resta Collection, then in the Robinson, Buhler and Koenigs Collection, later in Rotterdam's Boymans. Unanimously accepted as a Giorgione, but with reservations by Justi.

Plate 93a

THE VIOLA PLAYER. *Ink on paper, 19·4 × 14·6. Paris, École des Beaux-Arts*. Formerly in the Cosway and Mayor Collections. Kristeller believes it to be by Campagnola and some ascribe it to Titian, but the majority of modern critics (Hadeln, Justi, Suida, Fiocco, Morassi) attribute it to Giorgione.

Plate 93b

HEAD OF AN OLD MAN. *Paris, École des Beaux-Arts.* Drawing, originally believed to be by Perugino, but attributed to Giorgione by L. Venturi, who considers it a study for *The Three Philosophers*, and, with doubts, by Morassi.

Plates 94 and 95

FRAGMENT OF NUDE. *Fresco, approximately 250 × 140. Venice, Gallerie dell' Accademia.* This is one of Giorgione's frescos on the façade of the Fondaco dei Tedeschi in Venice. It was detached and restored in 1937 by Mauro Pellicioli. This is the only autograph evidence of those frescos, which included many male and female figures, mentioned by a number of eye-witnesses, and copied and engraved by A. M. Zanetti in his book, *Frescos by the most eminent Venetian Masters* (Venice, 1760), from which the reproductions on plates 94b and 95 are taken. Plate 94a shows the damaged fresco discussed in this context.

Plate 96a

THE HOROSCOPE. *Panel, 132 × 192. Dresden, Gemäldegalerie.* Originally considered a Giorgione, later described as a copy by Morelli, supported by A. Venturi, Berenson and practically all modern critics. L. Venturi and Swarzensky, for their part, claim that Giorgione has nothing to do even with this painting's original.

Plate 96b

THE FINDING OF PARIS. *Canvas, 20 × 30. Florence, Loeser Collection.* A copy, by David Teniers the Younger, of Giorgione's lost *Finding of Paris*, a fragment of which is shown in plate 23.

Plate 97a and b

JUDGEMENT OF PARIS. *Two canvases; 52·5 × 67·5 and 60 × 74. Dresden, Gemäldegalerie; Chiavari (Italy), Lanfranchi Collection.* Both copies of an original, now lost, recalled as a Giorgione by Ridolfi. Gronau and Hadeln believe that Domenico Campagnola painted the original; L. Venturi ascribes it to a late imitator; in Morassi's opinion the original was by Titian. Other copies of the same painting are to be found in Oslo's Larpendt Collection, at Malmesbury and in the Uffizi. Andrea Vendramin was the owner of yet another version. It is a fact that Paris was one of Giorgione's favorite subjects. (See also plates 104a and b.)

Plate 98

PAGE. *Panel, 23 × 30. Milan, Pinacoteca Ambrosiana.* Formerly in Cardinal Borromeo's Collection, it was donated to the Ambrosiana in 1618. The original title of the panel was *The Savior as a boy, playing with a ball,* and the painter was believed to be Andrea del Sarto. The work was later attributed to Giorgione and, by Fiocco, to Domenico Mancini. Wilde thought the subject to be Paris with the golden apple. Probably an ancient copy of a work by Giorgione.

PAINTINGS ATTRIBUTED TO GIORGIONE

Plate 99

HOMAGE TO A POET. *Panel, 59 × 48. London, National Gallery.* Formerly in the Aldobrandini and Bohn Collections, under the title *Solomon and his servants*; sold to the National Gallery in 1885. A. Venturi, having first attributed it to Giorgione, revised his opinion, and so did Cook, Justi, and the majority of other critics. Morassi sees this panel as "very closely connected with Giorgione". In fact, though here and there some aridity and triteness of treatment (such as the poet's laurels), may suggest the workshop's intervention, other aspects, such as the beautiful figure of the lute player, reveal the master's hand. Surely Giorgione was also responsible for the invention and the arrangement of masses.

Plate 100a

NATIVITY. *Panel, 91 × 115. Vienna, Kunsthistorisches Museum.* In Archduke Leopold Wilhelm's Collections in 1659 as a Giorgione. This is a replica, with some variations of landscape and in the trees seen on the left, of the *Allendale Nativity* (plate 33). For Fiocco it is the work of Giorgione but completed by others. Morassi sees in it an element of "tiredness" and believes that if the Allendale picture was one and the same as the *Night* of Vittorio Beccaro, this may be the other version seen in Taddeo Contarini's house.

Plate 100b

CERES. *Panel transferred to canvas, 70 × 54. Berlin, Kaiser Friedrich Museum.* In a recent paper, *Berliner Museen,* Zimmermann attributes this work to Giorgione, but his arguments are very disputable. Pallucchini insisted, verbally, on Sebastiano del Piombo. A comparison with the *Small nude* in Vienna, signed by Gerolamo da Treviso the Younger, might support the theory that this artist painted the original panel.

Plate 101

THE FINDING OF ROMULUS AND REMUS. *Panel, 69 × 121·5. Frankfurt, Staedel Institute.* Swarzensky discovered this panel in 1937, and Schwarzweller repainted it after a cleaning operation which damaged it considerably. The work, however, was unfinished, as revealed by the complexions of the faces, which leave bare the drawing underneath. The finished parts are the tree branches and leaves. Swarzensky attributed the panel to Giorgione, and the Gallery's Directors still accept the authorship. Richter is rather in favor of Giorgione's school, Fiocco of Campagnola and Morassi of Catena. Among the many landscapes with small figures comparable to the *Judgement of Solomon* and the *Trial of Moses* (plates 12 and 13), this is probably the best one and should also be compared with the Rasini *Judith* (plate 11). Similar but of a much lower standard, is the

53

Landscape with small figures, attributed to Giorgione by Morassi.

Plates 102–103

FOUR STORIES OF THYRSIS AND DAMON. *Two small panels, 45·5 × 20, each depicting two stories. London, National Gallery.* Bought in 1937 and attributed to Giorgione by Sir Kenneth Clark. Later ascribed by Borenius to Palma. Richter is supported by the great majority in attributing the panels to Previtali.

Plate 104

STORY OF PARIS. *Two small panels, each 45 × 66. Maidstone, Allington Castle, property of the heirs to Lord Conway.* These were formerly in the Albarelli Collection at Verona, from which they passed to the Duke of Ossuna, then to a merchant in St Jean-du-Luz and finally to Lord Conway. Cook thought them to be by Giorgione and his attribution was accepted by Monneret de Villard and later by Swarzensky and Schwarzweller, connecting them with the *Finding of Romulus and Remus* (plate 101). Lord Conway believes in Giorgione's authorship, but Gronau and Morassi attribute the panels to Catena, L. Venturi to a pupil of Lazzaro Bastiani, and Fiocco, rightly so, to Giulio Campagnola.

Plate 105

PORTRAIT OF GIOVANNI ONIGO. *Canvas, 68 × 55. Richmond, Cook Collection.* Formerly owned by the Onigo family in Treviso, later by the Florentine antique merchant, Volpi. In the Cook Collection since 1907. Attributed to Cariani by Borenius and Morassi, and correctly, to Pordenone by Fiocco.

Plate 106

PORTRAIT OF ANTONIO BROCCARDO. (More probably of Vittore Cappello). *Canvas, 72·5 × 54. Budapest Museum.* The faded inscription on the parapet reads: "Antonius Brokardus Marii f.", and is not original. The canvas comes from the collection of the Patriarch of Venice, Ladislao Pyrker, where it was described as a Titian. It is also attributed to Titian by Pulszky. Mündler describes it as by Francesco Morone; Frizzoni, as by Torbido; Ludwig, A. Venturi and Fabriczy attribute it to Bernardino Licino and Loeser to Cavazzola. The attribution to Giorgione was first proposed by Morelli, and followed—with reservations—by Thausing, Berenson, Cook, Justi and Fiocco. As in the case of the Onigo portrait (plate 105), Morassi favors Cariani. Frimmel's attribution to Pordenone appears the most reasonable because of the portrait's resemblance to the Onigo portrait.

Plate 107

GATTAMELATA PORTRAIT. *Canvas, 90 × 73. Florence, Uffizi Gallery.* Cavalcaselle attributes this work to Torbido; Gamba, followed by Borenius, to Cavazzola; Longhi to Giorgione. Gamba confirms now that the Cavazzola attribution appears to be the most acceptable. The metallic colors, the heavy polish, the rather hard, dry modeling discourage identification with the last Giorgione work, especially if one compares this portrait with the *Knight of Malta* (plate 85).

Plate 108

CONCERT. *Canvas, 76 × 99. Hampton Court, Royal Gallery.* Listed as a Giorgione in ancient inventories, this picture is often linked with *The Three Ages of Man* in the Pitti Palace Gallery (plate 109). Morassi sees it as product of Giorgione's school, but L. Venturi noticed a difference of quality which leads one to connect this canvas with the *Master and disciple* formerly in the Cook Collection. Both paintings are far closer to the art of Morto da Feltre. Berenson, however, publishes this picture as "early Giorgione".

Plate 109

THE THREE AGES OF MAN. *Panel, 62 × 77. Florence, Pitti Palace.* Formerly in Prince Ferdinand's Collection, as a product of the Lombard School. This is a puzzling work, with an incredible range of attributions, none of which is entirely convincing. Inghirami and Cavalcaselle believe it to be a Lotto; Morelli, Cook, Suida and, later, Morassi, attributed it to Giorgione; Logan and Gronau attributed it to Morto da Feltre; L. Venturi describes it as "superior to Morto and very Giorgionesque"; Fiocco and, at first, Pallucchini ascribed it to Torbido, but Longhi and, later, Pallucchini thought it by Bellini; Berenson thought it a very late Bellini, but recently published it as "early Giorgione".

The only fact of which we are sure is that this is the work of an unknown Master from the Veneto in the early sixteenth century.

Plate 110

VIRGIN AND CHILD. *Canvas, 44 × 36·5. Leningrad, Hermitage Museum.* Transferred from wood to canvas in 1872. Formerly thought to be by Giambellino's School or by Bissolo, it was first attributed to Giorgione in 1908 by Justi, who

changed his mind in 1936. Only Morassi accepted the attribution; Richter is not sure; Fiocco speaks of "Giorgione and restorers". One cannot fail to find a certain Giorgionesque atmosphere in this painting, but, among the many works attributed to the master, this one contains the greatest number of Flemish and Antonello influences. It should be ascribed to an unknown painter from the Veneto of the sixteenth century.

Plates 111–112

SINGER and THE MUSICIAN. *Canvases, respectively 112 × 77 and 101 × 75. Rome, Borghese Gallery.* Described as "Giorgione's two buffoons" by Manilli in his book, *Villa Borghese* (1650) and also in a 1693 inventory. An official document of 1833 mentions Giambellino. According to A. Venturi the painter was Domenico Capriolo; Longhi at first thought it by a member of Mancini's group, later ascribing it verbally to Giorgione. This suggestion was developed by Paola della Pergola who explicitly attributed the paintings to Giorgione, with the support of Luciana Ferrara, in 1954. A referendum was then held in which Fiocco insisted on Capriolo; Grassi, Wittgens, Longhi and Zeri voted for Giorgione; Gnudi, though generous in his praise of the quality of the two works, kept his own council. The author finds it difficult to reconcile these paintings with what must reasonably have been Giorgione's last style. Once Titian has been excluded, one should think rather of a provincial follower of Giorgione, who intensified the Master's vibrations and amplified his forms. Perhaps Savoldo, possibly Pordenone, but especially Dosso.

Plate 113

SHEPHERD WITH FLUTE. *Canvas, 52 × 98. Naples, Pinacoteca Nazionale.* Attributed by Berenson to Cariani and by Morassi to Sebastiano del Piombo. The author has reached the same conclusion here as in the case of the two previous works, though this canvas may not be by Dosso.

Plate 114

JUDGEMENT OF SOLOMON. *Canvas, 208 × 318, unfinished. Kingston Lacy (U.K.). Bankes Collection.* Attributed by Wickhoff to Stefano Cernotto, of the Bonifazio Veronese School; by Roger Fry to Catena; by Hourticq to Titian; by Suida, partly, to Sebastiano del Piombo and partly to Giorgione; by Fiocco entirely to Giorgione. Rightly, first L. Venturi, then Longhi, Pallucchini and Morassi attributed the canvas entirely to Sebastiano.

Plate 115

SACRED CONVERSATION. *Panel, 50 × 81. Venice, Gallerie dell' Accademia.* Formerly attributed to Cariani, then to Previtali, later still to a follower of Giambellino. Gronau and L. Venturi associated it with the *Allendale Nativity*, believed at the time to be by Catena, but now Venturi accepts the *Allendale Nativity* as a Giorgione. For Berenson the artist was Previtali; Longhi, followed by Morassi, suggested Giorgione; Pallucchini is decidedly in favor of Sebastiano del Piombo and Fiocco shares his view with reservations; for Dussler too, the painter is Sebastiano. Though admittedly there are some points of contact with the Louvre's *Sacred Conversation*—certainly by Sebastiano—and with the Glasgow *Adulteress*—probably by Sebastiano—the last attribution cannot be free of all doubt. Richter's suggestion of Palma should not be too lightly discarded.

Plate 116

SUSANNAH AND DANIEL (also known as *Christ and the Adulteress*). *Canvas, 137 × 180. Glasgow, Corporation Galleries.* This could be identified with the *Adulteress* described as "for sale and a work by Giorgione" in a letter by Camillo Sordi to Francesco Gonzaga Duke of Mantua in 1612. A copy by Cariani is in Bergamo's Accademia Carrara. The Glasgow painting had been attributed to Cariani by Cavalcaselle; to Domenico Campagnola by J. P. Richter; to Sebastiano, then to Titian, then to Giorgione by Berenson; to Romanino by A. Venturi and Gombosi; to Giorgione by Bode, Cook, Morelli, Justi and Hermanin; by L. Venturi, Pallucchini and generally the other moderns to Titian. Richter believes the canvas was begun by Giorgione and finished by Titian. In the author's view Sebastiano is more plausible.

Plate 117

CONCERT. *Canvas, 108 × 122. Florence, Pitti Palace.* Bought as a Giorgione in 1654 by Cardinal Leopoldo de' Medici, this painting could be the same one recalled by Ridolfi in the Florentine Collection of Paolo del Sera: attributed by Morelli to Titian, by Wickhoff and Hadeln to Domenico Campagnola, by Hourticq to Sebastiano del Piombo. Gronau believed it to have been begun by Giorgione and finished by Titian; in the opinion of many modern critics (Suida, Tietze, Morassi), it was painted entirely by

Titian. The old attribution to Giorgione is still accepted by Cook, Richter, Fiocco and now also by L. Venturi. The intense drama of the scene, however, the thin color paste, and especially the feverish eyes of the monk suggest very strongly the hand of Titian. Compare this canvas with Titian's Ancona *Madonna* and with the *Portrait* in the Lansdowne Collection.

Plate 118

PORTRAIT OF A MAN. *Canvas, 75 × 62·5. Washington, National Gallery of Art, Kress Collection.* Attributed to Giorgione by Cook, Borroughs, Morassi (with reservations), and, rightly so, to Titian by Berenson and L. Venturi. D. Phillips notes that "the facial expression, intense with the suggestion of inward conflict, and the structural simplification of the forms are eloquent of Giorgione".

Plate 119

ST GEORGE. *Panel, 124 × 65. Venice, Cini Collection.* Attributed to Giorgione by Waagen; Berenson calls it a fragment and claims that the Saint's head is modern. Borenius, Fiocco, Gronau, consider it a Palma, and Longhi believes it a Titian, painted about 1511. This appears the most acceptable attribution, but perhaps Titian painted it a few years later.

Plate 120

STORM AT SEA. *Canvas, 305 × 405. Venice, Gallerie dell'Accademia.* Recalled as by Giorgione by Vasari in the first edition of the *Lives*, and as by Palma in the second edition. This work, in extremely poor condition, is partly by Palma and partly by Paris Bordone.

Other works have been attributed to Giorgione, but with so little justification that they do not merit reproduction in this book. They are: *Portrait of a Della Rovere* (Vienna, Kunsthistorisches Museum: possibly by Pellegrino da San Daniele); *Portrait of Ariosto* (?) (London, National Gallery: Titian); *Portrait of a Grimani* (?) (New York, Metropolitan Museum: Titian); *Portrait of a Musician* (Rome, Palazzo Venezia: Titian); *Man in Fur Coat* (Munich Gallery: Palma); *The Bravo* (Vienna, Kunsthistoriches Museum: Palma); *Young Faun* (Munich Gallery: Palma); *Orpheus and Eurydice* (Bergamo, Accademia Carrara: Palma); *Apollo and Daphne* (Venice, Seminario; Palma); *Birth of Adonis* and *The Forest of Polydorus* (Padua, Museo Civico: both by Romanino); *Dead Christ* (Treviso, Monte di Pieta': Francesco Vecellio); *Portrait* (Paris, Gentilli Collection: perhaps by Pordenone); *Young Man* (Brunswick, Herzog Anton Ulrich Museum: School of Palma); *Portrait* (New York, Bache Collection: School of Palma); *Portrait* (Rome, Borghese Gallery: School of Pordenone).

WORKS MENTIONED BY SOURCES AND DOCUMENTS OF THE XVI AND XVII CENTURIES

INSCRIPTIONS:

1. June 5, 1506; *Laura* (plate 41).
2. 1508: *Portrait* (plate 90).

DOCUMENTS:

3. 1507: A *Telero* for the Audience Hall of the Doge's Palace (lost).
4. 1508: Frescos on the façade of the Fondaco dei Tedeschi (plates 94 and 95).

TADDEO ALBANO, letter of November 7, 1510:

5. *Night* (Creche), in the home of Taddeo Contarini (identified by some as the painting in plate 100a).
6. *Night* (Creche), in the home of Vincenzo Beccaro (identified by some as the painting on plate 33).

MARCANTONIO MICHIEL, *information about works of art:*

In the home of Taddeo Contarini, 1525:

7. "The canvas, in oils, of the three philosophers in a landscape, two standing and one sitting down, and contemplating the rays of the sun, with that stone so admirably painted, was begun by Zorzo of Castelfranco and finished by Sebastian the Venetian" (plate 48).
8. "The great oil canvas showing Aeneas and Anchises in Hades . . .", (identified by some with the painting in plate 21).
9. "The canvas of a landscape with the birth of Paris, and two shepherds standing by, was painted by Zorzo of Castelfranco and was one of his first works" (identified by some as the picture in plate 23; see also plate 96b).

In the home of Gerolamo Marcello, 1525:

10. "The portrait of the very same M. Hieronimo in arms, showing his back down to the waist, and turning his head" (lost).
11. "The canvas with the nude Venus, sleeping in a landscape, with a little Cupid by her side, was painted by Zorzo of Castelfranco, but the landscape and the Cupid were finished by Titian" (generally identified as the picture in plate 68).
12. "Half-length figure of Mr Hieronimo, reading" (lost).

In the home of Giannantonio Venier, 1528:

13. "Half-length figure of a soldier, armed but not wearing his helmet" (lost).

In the home of Gabriele Vendramin, 1530:

14. "The small canvas of a landscape, with a storm, a gypsy woman, and a soldier" (plate 54).
15. "The dead Christ upon his tomb, supported by an angel, was painted by Zorzo of Castelfranco and reconditioned by Titian" (mistakenly identified by some with the *Dead Christ* of Treviso).

In the home of Giovanni Ram, 1531:

16. "The head of a young shepherd with fruit in his hand" (lost).

17. "Head of a youth with an arrow in his hand" (generally identified as the picture in plate 63).

In the home of Antonio Pasqualino, January 5, 1532:

18. "The head of a lad holding an arrow in his hand was painted by Zorzo of Castelfranco, and Pasqualino has received it from Giovanni Ram, though Ram still possesses a copy of it, which he believes to be an original" (see above, n. 17).

19. "The head of St James with a pilgrim's staff was painted by Zorzo of Castelfranco, or copied by one of his pupils from the Christ in the Church of San Rocco." (The copy has been lost; the original is shown in plate 83.)

In the home of Andrea Oddoni, 1532:

20. "The nude St Jerome sitting in the desert in the moonlight was copied from a canvas by Zorzo of Castelfranco" (lost).

In the home of Michele Contarini, August 1543:

21. "The ink on paper nude in a landscape was drawn by Zorzo" (lost).

In the home of Marcantonio Michiel, August 1543:

22. ". . . This is the nude by Zorzo himself, which is in my possession" (lost).

In the home of Pietro Bembo, in Padua, undated:

23. "The two small paintings on goatskin, in vermilion, are by Giulio Campagnola; one is a nude woman copied from Zorzo, reclining and turned" (lost).

In the home of Pietro Servio, note added 1575:

24. "A portrait of his father by Zorzo of Castelfranco" (lost).

PAOLO PINO, *Dialogue on painting,* 1548:

25. "St George, whose figure is reflected in the water and, on the sides, by two mirrors" (lost).

LUDOVICO DOLCE, *Dialogue on Painting,* 1557:

26. "Frescos on the Fondaco dei Tedeschi" (see above, n. 4).

PARIS BORDONE, *evaluation in the Giovanni Grimani Home, 1563:*

27. "A crèche" (identified by some as the picture in plate 33).

VASARI, *Lives,* Second Edition, 1568:

In the home of the Patriarch of Aquileia, Grimani:

28. "A head for a David (said to be his own portrait), with hair coming down to the shoulders" (plate 62).

29. "A larger head of a man, holding in his hand the red beret of a Commander" (lost).

30. "The head of a cherub or boy, with hair like goatskin" (lost).

In the Borgherini home in Florence:

31. "The portrait of Giovanni as a young man and in the same picture the portrait of the master who was his teacher . . ." (lost).

In the home of Anton de' Nobili:

32. "The head of an armed captain, said to be one of the Captains which Consalvo Ferrante took with him to Venice" (lost).

In Consalvo Ferrante's home:

33. "The great Consalvo himself, armed" (lost).

Shown at the Fair on Ascension Day (1566?):

34. "Portrait of Leonardo Lore-dano . . . when he was Doge" (lost).

At Faenza, in the home of Giovanni (Bernardi) from Castelbolognese:

35. Portrait of Giovanni Bernardi's father-in-law (lost).

In the Soranzo home at San Polo:

36. Frescos on the façade with "many pictures and stories and other fanciful paintings of his . . . an oil painting on plaster . . . and a spring" (lost).

Fondaco dei Tedeschi

37. Frescos on the façade (see above, n. 4).

Church of San Rocco:

38. "Christ carrying the Cross, and a Jew pulling at Him" (see above n. 19).

Locality unknown:

39. "He painted a nude figure with its back turned to the spectator. At the feet of the figure a limpid stream reflected the front, while a mirror on one side and a burnished corselet on the other reflected the profiles. By this beautiful fancy Giorgione wished to prove that painting is the superior art, requiring more talent and greater effort." (See under Paolo Pino, n. 25.)

In the home of Giovanni Cornaro:

40. Portrait of Caterina Cornaro (lost).

In the home of Giorgio Vasari, from the "Book of drawings":

41. "A head painted in oils, copied from a German of the Fucheri family" (lost).

CARLO RIDOLFI, *The marvels of art,* 1648:

In the Parish Church of Castelfranco:

42. "The panel of Our Lady with Our Lord the Child . . . on the left side St George, in which he portrayed himself, and on the right side St Francis" (plate 42).

In Giorgione's home at San Silvestro:

43. On the façade "oval frescos, with musicians, painters and other fancies inside, and upon the chimneys groups of children . . . in chiaroscuro. . . . Two half-length figures it appears represent the Emperor Friedrich I and Antonia da Bergamo who, having gripped a dagger, is about to kill herself to protect her virginity" (lost).

In the Soranzo home at San Polo:

44. Frescos upon the façade: "stories, friezes, of child and figures in niches, . . . the figure of a woman with flowers in her hand, and in another the figure of Vulcan who is whipping Eros" (see above, n. 36).

In Paolo del Sera's home:

45. "Three portraits . . . upon the same canvas" (plate 117).

In the home of Grimani ai Servi:

46. Frescos on the façade with "nude women" (lost).

In Campo Santo Stefano:

47. Frescos of half-length figures upon a façade (lost).

House overlooking the Canal at Santa Maria Zobenigo:

48. Frescos on the façade "ovals with half-length figures of Bacchus, Venus or Mars . . . grotesques in chiaroscuro . . . and children" (lost).

60

In the Cassinelli home in Genoa:

49. "Allegories of human life and half-figures: 'nurse with child, armed warrior', a 'young man disputing with philosophers, among merchants and an old woman', 'an antique nude'" (lost).

In the home of Andrea Vendramin:

50. "Self-portrait as David holding Goliath's head, between a knight and a soldier" (lost).

FONDACO DEI TEDESCHI:

51. Frescos upon the façade (see above, n. 4).

In the Marcello home:

52. "A nude sleeping Venus, with Cupid at her feet and a small bird in her hand . . . finished by Titian" (see above, n. 11).

In the home of G. Battista Sanuto:

53. "Bust of woman in gypsy clothing" with her right hand on a book (lost).

In the Leoni home at San Lorenzo:

54. David giving the head of Goliath to Saul (lost).

55. Judgement of Paris (lost: there are many copies of it. See plates 97a and b).

In the Grimani home at San Marcuola:

56. Judgement of Solomon "with the Rabbi's figure unfinished" (identified by some as the picture in plate 114).

In the home of Cavalier Gussoni:

57. Madonna with St Jerome and other figures (lost).

In the home of Senator Domenico Ruzzini:

58. Portrait of a "Captain in armor" (lost).

In the Contarini home at San Samuele:

59. Portrait of a "Knight in black armor" (lost).

In the Malipiero home:

60. Half figure of St Jerome reading a book (lost).

In the home of Niccolo' Crasso:

61. Portrait of the philosopher Luigi Crasso (lost).

In the Annunciata Church at Cremona:

62. St Sebastian (lost).

In the home of Prince Aldobrandini in Rome:

63. Three-quarter length figure of St Sebastian (lost).

In the home of Prince Borghese in Rome:

64. David (lost).

In the home of the Muselli Family in Verona:

65. Young man in fur coat (lost).

In the home of the Van Voert family in Antwerp:

66. Self-portrait as David with the head of Goliath (see above n. 28).

67. Portrait of a "Commander" General (see above n. 29).

68. Portrait of a youth in armor, in which his hand is reflected (lost).

69. Portrait of a German of the Fulchera family, with a fox fur-coat, "seen from the side and turning about". (Probably the "Man in fur coat" attributed to Titian, now in Munich. See above, n. 41).

70. Half length of a nude "in green cloth" (lost).

In the Doge's Palace at Venice, Great Council Hall:

71. Episode of the Emperor Friedrich kissing the foot of Pope Alexander III (lost).

72. "Celius Plotius attacked by Claudius", half figures. (This is the so-called *Bravo*, by Palma, now in Vienna.)

73. "Portrait of an ancient King" (lost).

Unspecified localities:

74. Portrait of Doge Agostino Barbarigo (lost).

75. Portrait of Caterina Cornaro (see above, n. 40).

76. Portrait of the Great Consalvo (see above, n. 33).

77. Portrait of Doge Leonardo Loredano (see above, n. 34).

78. The doctoring of cats (lost).

79. Nude woman and shepherd with pipe (lost).

80. Twelve pictures portraying the story of Psyche (lost).

81. The ascent to Mount Calvary with Veronica (lost).

82. Large head of Poliphemus wearing a hat (lost).

83. "Cassones" with "fables from Ovid's Golden Age: Jupiter smiting the Giants; Deucalion and Pyrrha; the serpent Python killed by Apollo; Apollo and Daphne Io, Argus and Mercury; the death of Phaethon; Diana and Callisto; Mercury and Apollon's flocks; the rape of Europa; Cadmus in Thebes; Diana and Actaeon; Venus, Mars and Vulcan; the killing of Niobe's sons; Baucis and Philemon; Theseus and Ariadne; Alcides, Deianira and Nessus; the love story of Apollo and Hyacinth; the love story of Venus and Adonis." Some of these were "reduced to small panels" and made up of "many studies". (Probably the whole long description is just a literary essay on the part of Ridolfi, aimed at impressing his erudite contemporaries, with no concrete reference to particular works, with the exception of the following.)

In the home of the Vidmani family:

84. Cassone with stories of Adonis: "his birth, . . . his sweet embraces with Venus . . . his killing by a boar. . . ." (lost).

DAVID TENIERS, *Theatrum pictorium*, 1669:

In the collection of Archduke Leopold Wilhelm in Brussels:

85. "The birth of Paris" (see above, n. 9).

86. "The Ambush" (lost).

LOCATION OF PAINTINGS

AMSTERDAM

LANZ COLLECTION
Allegory of Chastity (plate 20).

BERLIN

KAISER FRIEDRICH MUSEUM
Portrait of a youth (plates 66, 67).
Ceres (plate 100b; attribution).

BOSTON

GARDNER MUSEUM
Christ carrying the Cross (plate 82).

BRUNSWICK

HERZOG ANTON ULRICH MUSEUM
Self-portrait (plate 62).

BUDAPEST

MUSEUM OF FINE ARTS
The Finding of Paris (plate 23; fragment).
Portrait of Antonio Broccardo (plate 106; attribution).

CASTELFRANCO VENETO

CHURCH OF SAN LIBERALE
Madonna with SS Francis and Liberale (plates 42, 43, 44, 45, 46).

CASA PELLIZZARI
Frescos (plates 2, 3, 4, 5, 6, 7, 8, 9, 10).

CASA ROSTIROLLA
Fresco (plate 1).

CHIAVARI

LANFRANCHI COLLECTION
Judgement of Paris (plate 97b; copy).

DRESDEN

GEMÄLDEGALERIE
Sleeping Venus (plates 68, 69, 70, 71).
The Horoscope (plate 96a; copy).
Judgement of Paris (plate 97a; copy).

FLORENCE

UFFIZI
Judgement of Solomon (plates 12, 14).
Trial of Moses (plates 13, 15).
Knight of Malta (plate 85).
Gattamelata Portrait (plate 107; attribution).

PITTI PALACE
The Three Ages of Man (plate 109; attribution).
Concert (plate 117; attribution).

LOESER COLLECTION
The Finding of Paris (plate 96b; copy).

FRANKFURT

STAEDEL INSTITUTE
The Finding of Romulus and Remus (plate 101; attribution).

GLASGOW

CORPORATION GALLERIES
Susannah and Daniel (plate 116; attribution).

HAMPTON COURT

ROYAL GALLERY

Bust of Shepherd with Pipe (plate 65).
Concert (plate 108; attribution).

KINGSTON LACY (U.K.)

BANKES COLLECTION

Judgement of Solomon (plate 114; attribution).

LENINGRAD

HERMITAGE

Judith (plates 38, 39).
Virgin and Child (plate 110; attribution).

LONDON

NATIONAL GALLERY

Adoration of the Magi (plates 25, 26, 27, 28, 29).
Man in Armor (plate 47).
Homage to a Poet (plate 99; attribution).
Four Stories of Thyrsis and Damon (plates 102, 103; attribution).

PRIVATE COLLECTION

Aeneas and Anchises (plate 21).

MADRID

PRADO

Madonna with SS Anthony of Padua and Roch (plates 80, 81).

MAIDSTONE

ALLINGTON CASTLE, CONWAY COLLECTION

Story of Paris (plate 104; attribution).

MILAN

PINACOTECA AMBROSIANA

Page (plate 98; copy).

RASINI COLLECTION

Judith (plate 11).

NAPLES

PINACOTECA NAZIONALE

Shepherd with flute (plate 113; attribution).

NEW YORK

FRICK COLLECTION

Portrait of a youth (plate 88).

DUVEEN BROTHERS COLLECTION

Portrait of a lady (plate 40).

NORTHAMPTON

CASTLE ASHBY, NORTHAMPTON COLLECTION

Country Landscape (plate 22b).

OXFORD

ASHMOLEAN MUSEUM

Madonna reading (plate 24 and color plate I).

PADUA

MUSEO CIVICO

Leda and the Swan (plate 16).
Pastoral Scene (plate 17).

PARIS

LOUVRE

"Concert Champêtre" (plates 72–73, 74, 75, 76, 77, 78, 79).

ÉCOLE DES BEAUX-ARTS

The Viola Player (plate 93a; drawing).
Head of an old man (plate 93b; drawing).

PRINCETON (New Jersey)

UNIVERSITY MUSEUM

Paris on Mount Ida (plate 22a).

RICHMOND

COOK COLLECTION

Portrait of Giovanni Onigo (plate 105; attribution).

ROME

PALAZZO VENEZIA

Double portrait (plate 89).

BORGHESE GALLERY

Singer (plate 111; attribution).
The Musician (plate 112); attribution.

ROTTERDAM

BOYMANS MUSEUM

View of Castelfranco (plate 92; drawing).

SAN DIEGO

FINE ARTS SOCIETY

Portrait of a man (plates 90, 91).

VENICE

ACCADEMIA

Gypsy and Soldier (plates 54, 55, 56, 57, 58, 59, 60 and color plate III).
Portrait of an old woman (plate 61 and color plate IV).
Fragment of a nude (plate 94a).
Sacred Conversation (plate 115; attribution).
Storm at Sea (plate 120; attribution).

CHURCH OF SAN ROCCO

Christ with Cross and other figures (plates 83, 84).

SPANIO COLLECTION

Warrior with Page (plates 86, 87).

CINI COLLECTION

St George (plate 119; attribution).

VIENNA

KUNSTHISTORISCHES MUSEUM

Portrait of Laura (plate 41).
The Three Philosophers (plates 48, 49, 50, 51, 52, 53 and color plate II).
Youth holding arrow (plate 63).
David with head of Goliath (plate 64)
Nativity (plate 100a; attribution).

WASHINGTON

NATIONAL GALLERY OF ART

Landscape with Nymph and Cupid (plate 19).
Holy Family (plates 30, 31, 32).
Allendale Nativity (plates 33, 34, 35, 36, 37).
Portrait of a man (plate 118; attribution).

PHILLIPS COLLECTION

Allegory of Time (plate 18).

SELECTED CRITICISM

I will shut the mouths of those who would defend sculpture, as did Giorgione da Castel Franco, our celebrated artist as good and worthy of honor as any of the ancient masters. He confounded for ever the sculptors by painting a picture of an armed St George standing with his feet near the edge of a limpid stream, into which all his figure was reflected; then he painted a mirror, set up against a tree trunk, which reflected the whole of the Saint's back and one side; he added another mirror opposite, which revealed the other side of St George, and thus he proved that a painter can show an entire figure at one glance, which a sculptor cannot do. This work of his was perfectly seen and understood as combining the three parts of painting, which are design, invention, and color. PAOLO PINO,
Dialogo di Pittura, 1548.

Now Giovanni Bellini and the other masters of that time were not accustomed to study the antique, but copied what they saw before them, and that in a dry, hard, labored manner, and this Titian also acquired.

But in or about 1507 Giorgione da Castelfranco, not liking this method, began to paint in a very beautiful manner. He did not neglect to work from life, or to use natural color, and he painted directly in color without a drawing. He held that this was the best way, shading with colder or warmer tints as the living object might demand. But in doing this he did not perceive that it is impossible to arrange a composition intelligibly without first sketching the forms and grouping them in different ways, for the fancy needs actually to see the design, in order to form a correct judgement. GIORGIO VASARI,
The Lives of the most eminent Architects, Painters and Sculptors of Italy from Cimabue to our days, First edition, 1550.

Then there was an artist greatly thought of, but of whom much more could have been expected, of whom we have seen some oil paintings so lively, and so fluid around the contours, that no shadows can be perceived. He died, this valiant man, of the plague, and his death was a great loss to art.

LODOVICO DOLCE,
L'Aretino, or *Dialogue on Painting*, 1557.

Giorgione had seen some works by Leonardo, in which the contours were made fluid, and tinged with dark in tremendous measure. This manner he liked so much that as long as he lived he constantly followed it, and imitated it considerably in his oils. As he enjoyed the pleasure of his creations, he strove continuously to put into his work the most beautiful and varied ideas that came to him. Nature had endowed him with such a benign spirit that both in oils and in his frescos he portrayed some very lively things, while other pictures were soft, and harmonic, and fluid in the dark areas, so that many who at the time were considered excellent artists admitted that Giorgione had been born to infuse spirit in his figures, and to reproduce the freshness of a live complexion better than anyone else, not only in Venice, but everywhere.

GIORGIO VASARI,
Lives, Second edition, 1568.

While Florence was acquiring fame thanks to Leonardo, so the name of Venice, thanks to the excellence of Giorgione da Castelfranco was ringing throughout the world. He was educated in Venice and applied himself so intensely to art that he surpassed in painting Giovanni and Gentile Bellini, and gave such life to his figures, that they looked alive.

RAFFAELLO BORGHINI,
Il Riposo, 1584.

Giorgione da Castelfranco was greatly fortunate in depicting fish under the limpid waters, and trees and fruits, and all that he chose, in a beautiful manner.

GIAN PAOLO LOMAZZO,
Treatise on the art of painting, 1584.

(*Poem in Venetian dialect, free translation*):

> Zorzon, you were the first, it is well known,
> To fashion marvels with your paints and brushes;
> And as long as the world and Men shall last
> Your greatness shall never be forgotten.
>
> Until you appeared, all other artists had
> Created statues, whilst you made live figures
> And with the magic of your colors you
> Have given them a truly human soul.

MARCO BOSCHINI,
The Chart of Pictorial Navigation, 1660.

In painting he discovered a softness of touch with the brushes that had never existed before him, and one must confess that his strokes are so much flesh and blood; but his manner, on the other hand, is so rich and easy that one cannot speak of pictorial fiction, but rather of natural reality, because in the softness of his contours, in the placing of lights and "mezze tinte", in the reds, in the strengthening or lowering of his hues, he created such a pleasing and faithful harmony that one should describe his art as painted Nature, or naturalized painting. The ideas of this artist are all solemn, majestic or important, corresponding as they do to his name of Giorgione, and that is why his genius was seen to be directed towards grave figures, with heavy berets upon their heads, with bizarreries of plumage, old-fashioned clothing, shirts that are visible under their tunics, and blown out sleeves with slits in them, breeches in the style of Giambellino but of a more beautiful shape; his materials are silk, velvet, damask, wide stripes of satin; other figures wear armors as polished as mirrors; his was the real Idea of human actions.

MARCO BOSCHINI,
The rich minefields of Venetian painting, 1664.

It is known to everyone that Giorgio, or Giorgione da Castel-franco, was one of the first of us to release painting from the narrowness of its previous conditions. It was he who gave to it the genuine character of art. By allowing his genius to wander freely he departed from the beaten track of simple reasoning, which can control only science, and added to solid knowledge the capricious flights of fancy in order to attract and to please. The very moment he had mastered the excellent principles, he began to feel the greatness of his genius, being as it was full of fire, and of a certain natural violence; thus he emerged flying from his old timidity and infused a life which had previously been lacking in the painted figure, however well organized this may have been by his masters. In his hands colors achieved an accomplished taste, and he succeeded in portraying to perfection the cool reality of real flesh. He gave a new rotundity and vigor to painted objects, and thanks to the liveliness of his spirit he achieved a veracity never seen before. Aptly, he flashed lights upon shadows, which always appear rather sharp in reality, and most of all handled his dark masses with complete freedom, at times cleverly increasing their intensity beyond the natural one, at other times, making them more tender and serene by giving them unity and softness of contour, so that the parts included between those masses could be seen and yet not seen. This method, to everybody's eyes, increased the greatness of the artist's style, though only few could understand the reason for it.

ANTON MARIA ZANETTI,
On Venetian Painting and Public works of the Venetian masters, 1771.

From the days of his apprenticeship in the Bellinis' workshop, and being guided by a spirit which knew its own strength, he disdained that pettishness which still prevailed, and replaced it with that freedom of action, almost with that contempt, which is the quintessence of art. In this he was an inventor, that no one before him had known that manner of handling the brush, so resolute and strong, so capable of surprising the eye, especially when it came to distances.

He then went on to make his manner greater, by broadening his contours, renovating his perspectives, giving life to the ideas

reflected in the faces and gestures, carefully selecting his draperies and accessories, softening his passages from one color to another, and finally by strengthening and giving much greater effect to his "chiaroscuro".   LUIGI LANZI,
History of Italian painting, 1796.

Giorgione was certainly a great artist, indeed one of the greatest that the Renaissance ever produced. On the other hand one cannot deny that there is a greatness which he could never achieve: the field of ascetic idealism never appealed to him. . . . But apart from this he was the inspirer of a revolution involving every branch of art, and which gave an exclusive character to the products of his vigorous brush.   ALEXIS-FRANCOIS RIO,
On Christian Art, 1836.

There could be reason for assuming that Giorgione was the first of Venetian moderns to follow in Bellini's footsteps and in attaching importance to the landscape. If we accept the tradition still alive in our days no one was his equal, at the end of the fifteenth century, in composing country scenes; no one could achieve the pure elegance of the figures which animated these landscapes. The landscapes familiar to Giorgione do not have the rocky character or the towering heights found by Titian in the Cadore region. No Dolomites project their sharp summits against the pure skyline; there are, instead, elms and cypresses, vines and mulberry-trees, hazel-bushes and poplars, graceful undulations, woods, farm-steads and battlements; and in all this there is variety, without repetitions.

CROWE and CAVALCASELLE,
History of Painting in Northern Italy, 1871.

By no school of painters have the necessary limitations of the art of painting been so unerringly though instinctively appre- hended, and the essence of what is pictorial in a picture so justly conceived, as by the school of Venice. . . . At last, with final mastery of all the technical secrets of his art, and with somewhat

more than "a spark of the divine fire" to his share, comes Giorgione. He is the inventor of "genre", of those easily movable pictures which serve neither for uses of devotion, nor of allegorical or historic teaching . . . morsels of actual life, conversation or music or play, but refined upon or idealized, till they come to seem like glimpses of life from afar. . . . He is typical of that aspiration of all the arts towards music, which I have endeavored to explain—towards the perfect indentification of matter and form.
WALTER PATER,
The School of Giorgione, 1877.

Giorgione did not display all his powers until the six last years of his short life, approximately from 1504 to 1511. In the few of his works which have come down to us . . . his original and eminently poetical intelligence shines so purely, his simple and honest artistic temperament speaks to us so strongly and attractively, that whomsoever has heard him once shall never forget him. No other painter can, as he, enrapture our fantasy with such an economy of means, and captivate our spirit for hours upon end; and yet, at times, we do not even know what his pictures mean.
IVAN LERMOLIEFF (G. MORELLI),
The Works of Italian Masters, 1880.

Giorgione's life was short, and very few of his works—not a score in all—have escaped destruction. But these suffice to give us a glimpse into that brief moment when the Renaissance found its most genuine expression in painting. Its overboisterous passions had quieted down into a sincere appreciation of beauty and of human relations. It would be really hard to say more about Giorgione than this, that his pictures are the perfect reflex of the Renaissance at its height.

BERNARD BERENSON,
The Venetian Painters of the Renaissance, 1894.

71

The problem of opened or closed contours was for Giorgione a motive of uncertainty. He had been trained by his master Giovanni Bellini to feel the beauty of a contour, even to prefer the refined beauty of a line. The magnificent oval of the Dresden Venus is still conceived as a closed contour, even though the delicate touch of its *sfumato* gives it a dreamlike quality. But when Giorgione added the soldier's figure to *Gypsy and Soldier*, he had no need for definite outlines, and in fact that image is typically a pictorial one, an open form, sketched out. . . .

This form of his which emerged from closed contours found its natural basis in the zones of color. And color was for Giorgione a conception of his fantasy even before becoming a feeling.

LIONELLO VENTURI,
Giorgione and Giorgionism, 1913.

The uncertainty of his craftsmanship is a further proof of how little Giorgione owed to the Venetian school. Even in the *Castelfranco Madonna*—the three figures of which, in spite of everything, are derived from Bellini's iconographic material— the faces and draperies belong to someone who, out of ignorance or contempt, would rather lose himself in his own innovations than follow the beaten road. A face, a wrinkle, a hand are difficulties that each and every craftsman has been taught to overcome; but surely it is not here that Giorgione proved himself a master. Apart from some problems to which he was able to find the solution—a rock, foliage, and especially some feminine faces—Giorgione will go down as a technician more curious than impeccable. And his weaknesses confer upon him a reputation for independence which certainly does not diminish him in the eyes of the moderns. Two particular reasons appear to justify his fame as an open innovator: his landscapes and his nudes, and also the combination of landscape and nude. Of all his landscapes the most beautiful is obviously the vision, so right and so new, of the Castelfranco walls growing pale under a thunderstorm. The man who was able to see and to portray such an effect is surely one of the painter-poets who have added to the poetry of nature the beauty of painting.

LOUIS HOURTICQ,
The Problem of Giorgione, 1930.

Some of his admirable creations appeared in the houses of the most exclusive lovers of art: intimately religious subjects; mythological, idyllic, fanciful themes—or at times hermetical compositions of a philosophical and literary nature—suddenly enriched the Venetian repertoire, pouring new blood into its trite iconography. A new spirit was being expressed in a lyrical, dream-like atmosphere, but this new spirit was also to the highest degree observant of nature in its most attractive and emotional aspects. A new taste for color was finding its way, vibrating with intensity of stress, and at the same time softened by an exquisite blending of tonalities.

This was a new light, enveloping everything in intangible gold-dust, and obtained by a technique so very different from the much vaunted Flemish method: this technique consisted in superimposing flashes of bright color to the chromatic structures beneath, or conversely in diminishing their brightness into an ashen-like blending of hues: this paved the way to Vecellio; these were the foundations of modern art.

ANTONIO MORASSI,
Giorgione, 1942.

Giorgione can only be understood in the light of Antonello da Messina. His great victory was in fact the addition of the Venetian chromatic taste to the Sicilian master's revelation; Giorgione brought into power Antonello's reform which, being free from the Flemish realistic minutia, was no longer compelled to "breathe big", and could finally adapt itself to a subtler, more idealistic and more human world, penetrating each fiber of it and exalting it with the power of color, finally aware of its constructive function.

His subtle passages from the generic to the specific, granting the same dignity to the landscape and figures, and respecting each person's individuality, for each one is a world; that movement of his picture inside the air, which came directly from his soul; that dramatic enveloping of each object with live atmosphere, was never fully appreciated, busy as people were with the dialectics of attribution.

So that, whereas a few undisputed and undisputable works would have sufficed—perhaps just the two pillars of the *Castelfranco Madonna* and of the *Gypsy and Soldier*—to prove that Giorgione was both renovated and a renovator, the student of this master has to proceed among the shifting sands of the various theories and sympathies, where it is easy to become bogged down, and not difficult to sink for ever.

GIUSEPPE FIOCCO,
Giorgione, 1942.

Giorgione's art is certainly a complex one in its developments, in its aesthetical interests and in its cultural values, so much so that from its origins it caused many different interpretations of its figures, many contradictions and numerous reactions in the field of historiography. Giorgione's taste is not as exclusive as Tintoretto's or Carpaccio's: from the nucleus of his inspiration —strictly connected with color and light, and therefore to tonality—an ever changing jet of invention spurts forth, possibly taking different directions. Giorgione's cultural thirst, based upon his interest in the currents of his time, had the gift, common to all geniuses, of expressing itself on every occasion, through a purely fantastic and lyrical process, in a perfect work of art. The practical result of this sensitivity of his, for ever active, was that in the field of invention all the links with the iconographic tradition of the fifteenth century, both religious and profane, were broken. With Giorgione a new representational mythology was born, in which man was put in touch with nature, to the extent where nature itself at times chose to become a protagonist;

a new dignity enriched the characters' psychology and they, in their isolation, became introspective. . . . His revolution in the artistic field consisted not only in a transformation of his subjects, but in a total renewal of representational sensitivity.

RODOLFO PALLUCCHINI,
Venetian Painting of the 16th Century, 1944.

His timidity was still present when he painted the Castelfranco Altarpiece, a composition which, far from being a revolutionary discovery, did not more than replace the old and sublime perspective formula of Bellini with the one, elegantly decorative —between ogival and pyramidal—so familiar to the traditions of Umbria and Emilia in the last decades of the fifteenth century, with what advantage I would not dare to say. . . .

These first cautious experiments of Giorgione the "pre-Raphaelite" lasted till he painted the *Gypsy and Soldier*. This work also is rather bound and, here and there, difficult to read, nor is it entirely free from the Emilian influences but . . . as a whole it indicates a return to the traditional chromatic principles of Venice, and an approaching change, perhaps even a reversal, of the master's previous experiences.

This reversal was perfectly understood, biographically speaking, by Vasari who, when writing about Giorgione at the beginning of his *Life of Titian*, made a completely different statement from the previous one. Had he forgotten that he had already described Giorgione as a follower of Leonardo's *sfumato*? He had not forgotten, but now he was referring to the second and last Giorgione, the Giorgione of the "modern manner", even though such a manner was exactly the opposite of that of Raphael and Michelangelo.

ROBERTO LONGHI,
Five centuries of Venetian Painting, 1946.

That intimate concentration of each single figure, that suspension of all movement, that silence, are all expressions of Giorgione's feeling as opposed to Titian's. This exuberant artist (Titian) reveals from his very first works a search for movement, for eloquence of gesture, peasant models, overladen draperies, tricks of light due perhaps to a passing cloud or two, crowded compositions. But here (in Giorgione's works), all is calm, spiritual concentration, sense of space, harmony of rich and intense colors.

CARLO GAMBA,
"My Giorgione", in Arte Veneta, 1954.

BIBLIOGRAPHICAL NOTE

The main source of information about Giorgione's works is the so called *Anonimo Morelliano*, by M. A. Michiel, the correct title of which is *Notizie d'opere sul disegno*; this was written between 1525 and 1543, and published by J. Morelli in 1800. For further biographical information about the artist the reader is advised to refer to the exemplary *Giorgione* by Antonio Morassi Milan, 1942), the bibliography for which goes as far as 1939. The author lists below only the milestones in critical literature on Giorgione, with the addition of the most recent works.

B. CASTIGLIONE. *Il Cortegiano*, Venice 1524.
P. PINO. *Dialogo di pittura*, Venice 1548.
G. VASARI. *Le Vite*, Florence 1550; second edition, Florence 1568.
L. DOLCE. *Dialogo della pittura*, Venice 1557.
R. BORGHINI. *Il riposo*, Florence 1584.
G. P. LOMAZZO. *Trattato dell'arte della pittura*, etc., Milan 1584.
C. RIDOLFI. *Le maraviglie dell'arte*, Venice 1648.
M. BOSCHINI. *La carta del navegar pitoresco*, Venice 1660.
M. BOSCHINI. *Le ricche minere della pittura veneziana*, Venice 1664.
J. VON SANDRART. *Academia nobilissimae artis pictoriae*, Nuremberg 1675.
A. M. ZANETTI. *Varie pitture a fresco de' principali Maestri veneziani*, Venice 1760.
A. M. ZANETTI. *Della pittura veneziana*, etc., Venice 1771.
L. LANZI. *Storia pittorica dell'Italia*, Bassano 1795–6.
J. A. CROWE and G. B. CAVALCASELLE. *A History of Painting in North Italy*, London 1871.
W. PATER. *The School of Giorgione*, London 1877.
I. LERMOLIEFF (G. MORELLI). *Die Werke italienischer Meister*, etc., Leipzig 1880.
A. CONTI. *Giorgione*, Florence 1894.
B. BERENSON. *The Venetian Painters of the Renaissance*, New York 1894.
C. VON FABRICZY. "Giorgione de Castelfranco", in *Repertorium für Kunstwissenschaft* 1896.
H. COOK. *Giorgione*, London 1900.
U. MONNERET DE VILLARD. *Giorgione da Castelfranco*, Bergamo 1904.
L. JUSTI. *Giorgione*, Berlin 1908.
G. GRONAU. "Kritische Studien zu Giorgione", in *Repertorium für Kunstwissenschaft* 1908.
L. VENTURI. *Giorgione e il Giorgionismo*, Milan 1913.
A. VENTURI. *Storia del'Arte Italiana*, IX, 3, Milan 1928.
L. HOURTICQ. *Le problème de Giorgione*, Paris 1930.
J. WILDE. Roentgenaufnahmen der "Drie Philosophen", etc., in *Oesterreiches Jahrbuch N. F.* 1932.

77

A. FERRIGUTO. *Attraverso i misteri di Giorgione*, Castelfranco 1933.

G. M. RICHTER. *Giorgio da Castelfranco, called Giorgione*, Chicago 1937.

L. COLETTI. "La crisi manieristica nella pittura veneziana", in *Convivium* 1941.

G. FIOCCO. *Giorgione*, Bergamo 1942.

A. MORASSI. *Giorgione*, Milan 1942.

G. DE BATZ. *Giorgione and his Circle*, Baltimore 1942.

R. PALLUCCHINI. *La pittura veneziana del Cinquecento*, I, Novara 1944.

V. MARIANI. *Giorgione*, Rome 1945.

R. LONGHI. *Viatico per cinque secoli di pittura veneziana*, Florence 1946.

L. COLETTI. "La crisi giorgionesca", in *Le Tre Venezie* 1947.

R. WISCHNITZER-BERNSTEIN. "The *Three Philosphers* by Giorgione", in *Gazette des Beaux-Arts*, 1945.

H. TIETZE. "La mostra di Giorgione e la sua cerchia a Baltimore", in *Arte Veneta* 1947.

G. GLÜCK. *Der Weg zum Bild*, Vienna 1948.

H. D. GRONAU. "Pitture veneziane in Inghilterra", in *Arte Veneta* 1949.

K. T. PARKER. *The Tallard "Madonna" in the Ashmolean Museum*, London 1949.

R. PALLUCCHINI. "Un nuovo Giorgione a Oxford", in *Arte Veneta* 1949.

H. TIETZE and E. TIETZE-CONRAT. The *Allendale Nativity*, etc., in *Art Bulletin* 1949.

R. L. DOUGLAS. "Some early Works of Giorgione", in *Art Quarterly* 1950.

R. MARINI. *Giorgione*, Trieste 1950.

F. M. GODFREY. "The Birth of Venetian Genre and Giorgione", in *The Connoisseur* 1951.

A. MORASSI. "The Ashmolean *Reading Madonna* and Giorgione's Chronology", in *Burlington Magazine* 1951.

G. CREIGTON. "On Subject and Non-Subject in Italian Renaissance Pictures", in *Art Bulletin* 1952.

P. DELLA PERGOLA. "Due nuovi Giorgioni", in *Paragone* 1953.

L. COLETTI. *La pittura veneta del Quattrocento*, Novara 1953.

G. FIOCCO, L. GRASSI, R. LONGHI, F. WITTGENS. Answering a referendum, in *La Scuola* 1954.

L. VENTURI. *Giorgione*, Rome 1954.

B. BERENSON. "Notes on Giorgione", in *Arte Veneta* 1954.

W. SUIDA. "Spigolature giorgionesche", in *Art Veneta* 1954.

P. HENDY. "More about Giorgione's *Daniel and Susannah* at Glasgow", in *Arte Veneta* 1954.

C. GAMBA. "Il mio Giorgione", in *Arte Veneta* 1954.

A. MORASSI. "Esordi di Tiziano", in *Arte Veneta* 1954.

M. VALSECCHI. *La Pittura veneziana*, Milan, 1954.

L. COLETTI. "Un tema giorgionesco", in *Emporium* 1955.

78

REPRODUCTIONS

ACKNOWLEDGEMENT FOR PLATES

Plates 1–10, 58, 59 and 94a: *Fiorentini, Florence*. Plate 11: *Zani, Milan*. Plates 12, 13, 54–56, 60, 61, 80, 81, 83, 84, 105, 109 and 117: *Anderson, Rome*. Plates 14, 15, 42–46, 68–79, 85, 107 and 120: *Alinari, Florence*. Plate 18: *Schaefer & Son, Baltimore*. Plates 23 and 101: *Bildarchiv Foto, Marburg*. Plates 62, 96a and 97a: *Bruckmann, Monaco*. Plate 65: *Ministry of Works, London*. Plates 66 and 67: *Sciaffusa Museum*. Plates 86 and 87: *A.F.I. Venice*. Plates 89 and 111–113: *Gabinetto Fotografico Nazionale, Rome*. Plate 93a: *Giraudon, Paris*. Plate 98: *Brogi, Florence*. Plate 100b: *Steinkopf, Berlin*. Plate 108: *Cooper, London*. Plate 115: *Bohm, Venice*. Transparencies for plates 21, 93b, 96b, 97b and 114 were kindly provided by the *Photographic Archives of the Pinacoteca di Brera, Milan*; and for plate 57 by *Mauro Pellicioli*. All other black and white transparencies were supplied by the respective Galleries and Museums. Color plates I and II are taken from *Studio dell'Illustrazione* by *F. Arborio Mella, Milan*; color plates III and IV are by *Giacomelli, Venice*.

Plate I. MEDALLION WITH HEAD OF MAN,
Castelfranco, Casa Rostirolla

SOLA VIRTVS
CLARA
AETERNA
QVE
HABETVR

VMBRI
TRANSITVS
EST
TEMPVS
NOSTRVM

Plate 2. FRESCOS, Castelfranco, Casa Pellizzari

Plate 3. FRESCOS, Castelfranco, Casa Pellizzari

SI
PRVDENS
ESSE
CVPIS
INSPICIVM
INTENDE

Plate 4. FRESCOS, Castelfranco, Casa Pellizzari

Plate 5. FRESCOS, Castelfranco, Casa Pellizzari

TE.... T.
O.. NIA
TEMP...

Plate 6. FRESCOS, Castelfranco, Casa Pellizzari

Plate 7. Details of plates 4 and 2

Plate 8. *Details of plates 2 and 3*

Plate 9. *Details of plates 3 and 5*

Plate 10. *Detail of plate 4*

Plate 11, JUDITH, Milan, Rasini Collection

Plate 12. JUDGEMENT OF SOLOMON, Florence, Uffizi

Plate 13. TRIAL OF MOSES, Florence, Uffizi

Plate 14. *Detail of plate 12*

Plate 15. *Detail of plate 13*

Plate 16. LEDA AND THE SWAN, Padua, Museo Civico

Plate 17. PASTORAL SCENE, Padua, Museo Civico

Plate 18. ALLEGORY OF TIME, Washington, Phillips Collection

Plate 19. LANDSCAPE WITH NYMPH AND CUPID,
Washington, National Gallery of Art

Plate 20. ALLEGORY OF CHASTITY, Amsterdam, Lanz Collection

Plate 21. AENEAS AND ANCHISES, London, Private Collection

Plate 22. PARIS ON MOUNT IDA,
Princeton, University Museum,
and COUNTRY LANDSCAPE,
Northampton, Castle Ashby

Plate 23. THE FINDING OF PARIS, Budapest, Fine Arts Museum

Plate 24. MADONNA READING,
Oxford, Ashmolean Museum (*detail of color plate I*)

Plate 25. ADORATION OF THE MAGI, London, National Gallery

Plate 26. *Detail of plate 25*

Plate 27. *Detail of plate 25*

Plate 28. *Detail of plate 25*

Plate 29. *Detail of plate 25*

Plate 30. HOLY FAMILY, Washington, National Gallery of Art

Plate 31. *Detail of plate 30*

Plate 32. *Detail of plate 30*

MADONNA READING, Oxford, Ashmolean Museum

Plate 33. ALLENDALE NATIVITY,
Washington, National Gallery of Art

Plate 34. *Detail of plate 33*

Plate 35. *Detail of plate 33*

Plate 36. *Detail of plate 33*

Plate 37. *Detail of plate 33*

Plate 38. JUDITH, Leningrad, Hermitage

Plate 39. *Detail of plate 38*

Plate 40. PORTRAIT OF A LADY,
New York, Duveen Brothers Collection

Plate 41. PORTRAIT OF LAURA,
Vienna, Kunsthistorisches Museum

Plate 42. MADONNA WITH SS FRANCIS AND LIBERALE,
Castelfranco, Church of San Liberale

Plate 43. *Detail of plate 42*

Plate 44. *Detail of plate 42*

Plate 45. *Detail of plate 42*

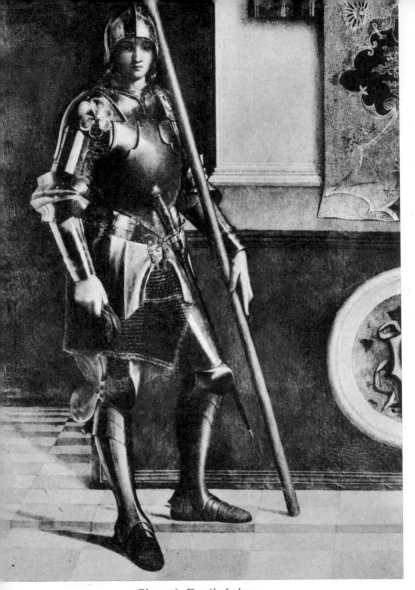

Plate 46. *Detail of plate 42*

Plate 47. MAN IN ARMOR, London, National Gallery

Plate 48. THE THREE PHILOSOPHERS,
Vienna, Kunsthistorisches Museum

THE THREE PHILOSOPHERS, Vienna, Kunsthistorisches Museum
(*detail of plate 48*)

Plate 49. *Detail of plate 48*

Plate 50. *Detail of plate 48*

Plate 51. *Detail of plate 48*

Plate 52. *Detail of plate 48*

Plate 53. *Detail of plate 48*

Plate 54. GYPSY AND SOLDIER, Venice, Accademia

Plate 55. *Detail of plate 54*

Plate 56. *Detail of plate 54*

GYPSY AND SOLDIER, Venice, Accademia (*detail of plate 54*)

Plate 57. *X-ray of part of plate 54*

Plate 58. *Detail of plate 54*

Plate 59. *Detail of plate 54*

Plate 60. *Detail of plate 54*

Plate 61. PORTRAIT OF AN OLD WOMAN,
Venice, Accademia (*detail of color plate IV*)

Plate 62. SELF-PORTRAIT,
Brunswick, H. Anton Ulrich Museum

Plate 63. YOUTH HOLDING ARROW,
Vienna, Kunsthistorisches Museum

Plate 64. DAVID WITH HEAD OF GOLIATH,
Vienna, Kunsthistorisches Museum

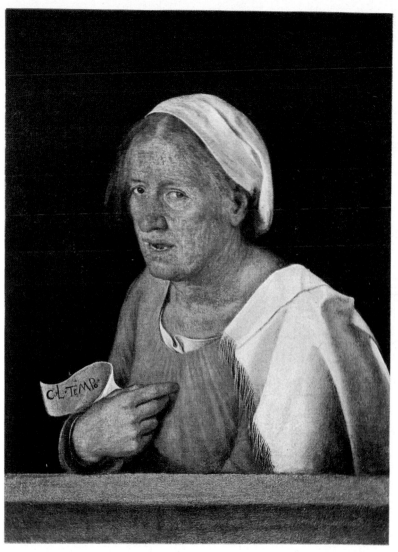

PORTRAIT OF AN OLD WOMAN, Venice, Accademia

Plate 65. PORTRAIT OF SHEPHERD WITH PIPE,
Hampton Court, Royal Gallery

V · V

Plate 66. PORTRAIT OF A YOUTH,
Berlin, Kaiser Friedrich Museum

Plate 67. *Detail of plate 66*

Plate 68. SLEEPING VENUS, Dresden, Gemäldegalerie

Plate 69. *Detail of plate 68*

Plate 70. *Detail of plate 68*

Plate 71. *Detail of plate 68*

Plate 72–73. "CONCERT CHAMPÊTRE", Paris, Louvre

Plate 74. *Detail of plates 72–73*

Plate 75. *Detail of plates 72–73*

Plate 76. *Detail of plates 72–73*

Plate 77. *Detail of plates 72–73*

Plate 78. *Detail of plates 72–73*

Plate 79. *Detail of plates 72–73*

Plate 80. MADONNA WITH SS ANTHONY OF PADUA AND ROCH, Madrid, Prado

Plate 81. *Detail of plate 80*

Plate 82. CHRIST CARRYING THE CROSS,
Boston, Gardner Museum

Plate 83. CHRIST WITH CROSS AND OTHER FIGURES,
Venice, Church of San Rocco

Plate 84. *Detail of plate 83*

Plate 85. KNIGHT OF MALTA, Florence, Uffizi

Plate 86. WARRIOR WITH PAGE, Venice, Spanio Collection

Plate 87. *Detail of plate 86*

Plate 88. PORTRAIT OF A YOUTH,
New York, Frick Collection

Plate 89. DOUBLE PORTRAIT,
Rome, Palazzo Venezia

Plate 90. PORTRAIT OF A MAN,
San Diego, Fine Arts Society

Plate 91. *Detail of plate 90*

Plate 92. VIEW OF CASTELFRANCO, Rotterdam, Boymans Museum (drawing)

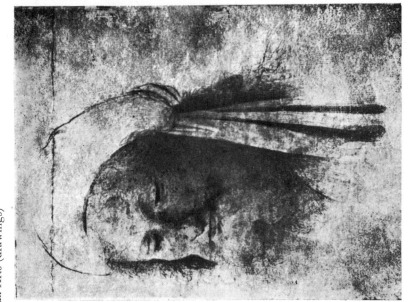

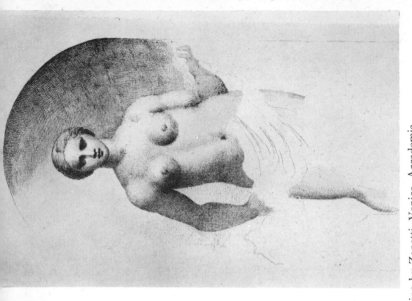

Plate 94. FRAGMENT OF NUDE *and* Engraving by Zanetti, Venice, Accademia

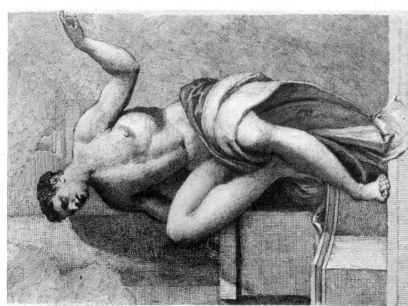

Plate 95. NUDES, engravings by Zanetti, Venice, Accademia

Plate 96. THE HOROSCOPE, Dresden, Gemäldegalerie
and THE FINDING OF PARIS, Florence, Loeser Collection (*copies*)

Plate 97. JUDGEMENT OF PARIS,
Dresden, Gemäldegalerie and Chiavari,
Lanfranchi Collection (*copies*)

Plate 98. PAGE, Milan,
Pinacoteca Ambrosiana (*copy*)

Plate 99. HOMAGE TO A POET,
London, National Gallery (*attrib.*)

Plate 100. NATIVITY, Vienna, Kunsthistorisches Museum, *and* CERES, Berlin, Kaiser Friedrich Museum (*attrib.*)

Plate 101. THE FINDING OF ROMULUS AND REMUS, Frankfurt,
Staedel Institute (*attrib.*)

Plate 102. STORIES OF THYRSIS AND DAMON,
London, National Gallery (*attrib.*)

Plate 103. STORIES OF THYRSIS AND DAMON, London, National Gallery (*attrib.*)

Plate 104. STORY OF PARIS,
Maidstone, Conway Collection (*attrib.*)

Plate 105. PORTRAIT OF GIOVANNI ONIGO
Richmond, Cook Collection (*attrib.*)

Plate 106. PORTRAIT OF ANTONIO BROCCARDO,
Budapest, Fine Arts Museum (*attrib.*)

Plate 107. GATTAMELATA PORTRAIT,
Florence, Uffizi (*attrib.*)

Plate 108. CONCERT, Hampton Court, Royal Gallery (*attrib.*)

Plate 109. THE THREE AGES OF MAN, Florence, Pitti Palace (*attrib.*)

Plate 110. VIRGIN AND CHILD,
Leningrad, Hermitage (*attrib.*)

Plate 111. SINGER, Rome, Borghese Gallery (*attrib.*)

Plate 112. THE MUSICIAN,
Rome, Borghese Gallery (*attrib.*)

Plate 113, SHEPHERD WITH FLUTE,
Naples, Pinacoteca Nazionale (*attrib.*)

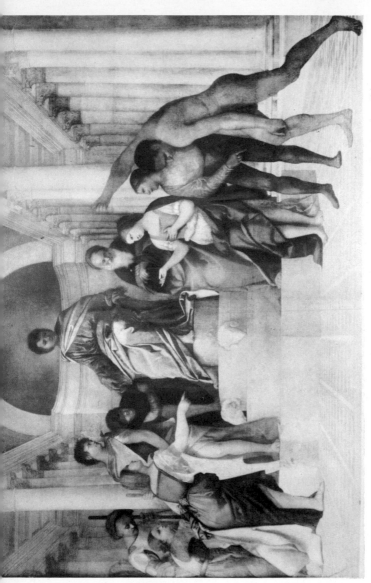

Plate 114, JUDGEMENT OF SOLOMON, Kingston Lacy, Bankes Collection (*attrib.*)

Plate 115. SACRED CONVERSATION, Venice, Accademia (*attrib.*)

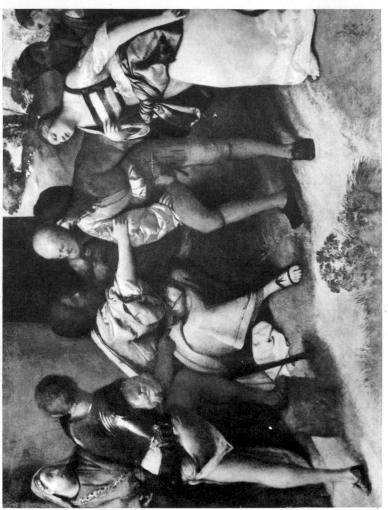

Plate 116. SUSANNAH AND DANIEL, Glasgow, Corporation Galleries (*attrib.*).

Plate 117. CONCERT, Florence, Pitti Palace (*attrib.*)

Plate 118. PORTRAIT OF A MAN,
Washington, National Gallery of Art (*attrib.*)

Plate 119. ST GEORGE, Venice, Cini Collection (*attrib.*)

Plate 120. STORM AT SEA,
Venice, Accademia (*attrib.*)